THE IVY YEARS

By the same author

THE IVY YEARS

GRASS ROOTS

VALLEY IN ARMS

BIG BEN

CAREER COACH

THE BACKFIELD FEUD

COMPOSING STICKS AND MORTAR BOARDS

With Ernest E. McMahon

THE CHRONICLES OF COLONEL HENRY

Edited with Richard Ellis

BOOKMAKING AND KINDRED AMENITIES

The Ivy Years

Earl Schenck Miers

NEW BRUNSWICK

Rutgers University Press

MCMXLV

For

DAVID *and* MEREDITH

—and for Mom, too

CONTENTS

CONTENTS

INTRODUCTION

Many times in this book the name of Earl Reed Silvers appears. During the past year Dr. Silvers has become dean of men on the campus here at New Brunswick, and a large majority of his waking hours (and more than a few of the hours that normally should be given over to slumber) now are devoted to the problems of boys in college. To the reader of this book it will be understandable why not so many days ago Dean Silvers and I discussed many of these problems—across the top of the old mahogany desk where some thirteen years ago he used to lecture to our junior class in short story writing. In those pleasant prewar years that class was one of our favorites, for it was concerned largely with people in terms of the little unpredictable acts, wise or foolish, that set people apart as individuals and make them more important than all the theories and platitudes that can be advanced as the obviously sensible patterns for human behavior.

A dean of men quickly discovers that in dealing with the undergraduate problems which fill every day on a university campus the human equation comes first. How else can you deal with the boy who has been betrayed by his own intellectual immaturity? Or with the boy who simply cannot wake up for his eight o'clock classes despite the astonishing fact that during these months of wartime shortages he owns three alarm

clocks? Or with the boy who will fail a course because of plagiarism on a book report; or with the boy who has become
irascible, in an academic sense, because of a professor's tiresome puns? The wonderfully rewarding part of an educator's
work is the fact that sooner or later most boys see beyond the
problems which beset their youth. Then they become like
the lad we can call Jim, who has decided quite on his own to
attend Sunday services in the Chapel despite the fact that he
is twenty-one and free to do as he pleases; or the lad we can
call Bill, who all at once has somehow awakened intellectually and no longer is a borderline case scholastically; or the lad
we can call Steve, who dreamed of college as a Marine in combat in the Pacific isles and now is having his dream fulfilled
through the G. I. Bill of Rights. Education offers no more
compelling challenge than the discovery that its principal in-
gredient is not books or classes or educational theories, but
simply undergraduates—undergraduates of all ages, of various backgrounds and varying degrees of intellectual preparation and receptivity, who take what they can from the educative process and give back to humanity through their ability to serve humanity the fruits of the entire labor. Nobody
can be more keenly aware of this truth than a dean of men;
if he is a competent dean of men, he is closer to the real pulsebeat of education than any other individual on the campus.

After sixteen years on a university campus, four as an undergraduate and twelve as a servant of the institution, affection naturally colors my respect for the tasks of education.
But the student as a human being still strikes me as almost
the whole of the question as to whether or not the educative
process is successful. After all, he is the one who must study
the curriculum, no matter who devises it or in what form it
is presented; he is the one who will judge by actual results
whether the men who have instructed him have led him to
the mental awakening so essential to his growth into man-
hood; he is the one who comes to the university campus to

begin a quest along strange and devious paths where, as he
walks, sometimes with happy comrades, sometimes in the
lonely desperation of his own conscience, he has nothing more
important to discover than himself. No one can promise that
the revelations which will come to him during these ivy years
will all be pleasant; no one can say that he will have the high
heart or the firm purpose to complete the adventure; no one
can predict what fine triumphs will be won or what sad heart-
breaks sustained. There will be many who will try to help
him, a few who will believe in him, and perhaps some who
will not. Here he will meet the great scholar and the occasional quack, and he will have to learn how to discriminate
between the one and the other. Here he will rub elbows with
the man of genius and with the man sunk helplessly in the rut
of mediocrity, and he will have to understand the great lessons
that each can teach. Here he will walk with idealist and cynic,
and by both will be influenced, according to his own good
sense and quickness of wit. The experience will be the same
on every campus and in every land where a free system of education exists; the undergraduate who understands so little
about academic matters—and likely wishes he knew less—
must in the final analysis receive the first benefit, the best
benefit, of the educative process.

If you have talked to boys in college, if you have given
them the chance to pour out their hearts and become their
natural selves, you cannot but respect the fine promise of these
boys. If you know the men who work on the campus, if you
are close to the basic seriousness and the healthy idealism that
underlies good teaching, you cannot doubt that the campus
is the right place for these boys to be. And if there exists a
limbo where these two groups sometimes fail to understand
each other completely, the teachers and the undergraduates,
that limbo exists in the main because of a difference in perspective—between the bird's eye view of the teacher who looks
down on the educative process with understanding and the

worm's eye view of the undergraduate who looks up in the hope of some day understanding.

This book is concerned almost entirely with the worm's eye view. Why the educative process exists as it does is not the province of its pages; the fact is accepted that it does exist, with many advantages and some limitations, and the student going off to college today, tomorrow, or a year or two hence must accept the circumstances as he finds them and do as well with them as he can. Education to him is certainly something far removed from theory; it is something he lives, in and out of the classroom, twenty-four hours a day. In the end his education becomes a series of situations, and how he reacts in those situations determines the nature and the quality of his education. The impulse to learning is something that must come from within himself rather than from without; the discipline of learning is never half so effective as the imitative inspiration of good teaching; there is very little that can be superimposed upon a normal boy beyond his hat.

Education from the worm's eye view—the one common attitude toward education that all of us enjoy at one time or another—is concerned with recognizing the patterns from which the knowledge we ultimately possess is gained. On a university campus those patterns fall into a number of situations, as the chapters of this book fall into a number of situations, which are typical and constant: making friends, fraternity and dormitory life, the classroom and laboratory, relations with the faculty, bull sessions, spiritual growth, study, the fellowship of books, extracurricular activities, campus politics, hell raising, student part-time employment, the intellectual awakening, and scholastic standards, among others. The educative process is the common denominator of all these experiences; they comprise the worm's eye view, and give it meaning in terms of the student and of humanity. From all these situations must come the self-discovery which, when all is said, represents the student's education. Perhaps the painful and often unprofitable process of trial and error is the only way of making this self-discovery; but when you talk to boys in college about the meaning and purpose of college, the conviction persists that if they could see re-created in advance the patterns of experience by which they must guide their course through the ivy years, they would know sooner whither they were bound and for what high, rich purpose.

This book is in its entirety autobiographical; buildings and places are named as they exist; and members of the faculty are presented by name. There is an element of fiction in that the author has called himself Jeremy Baxter and has similarly disguised the real identity of his college mates, feeling that the cause of honesty was better served in this manner, but there is very little fiction in the incidents related. In being one man's story certain limitations naturally were imposed in the writing of this book, but they were limitations of scope rather than of meaning. One example will suffice. Nowhere in these pages are athletics treated other than as they are seen by the student who is only a spectator. The athletic coach can at once complain that this is a serious omission, for is not any athletic team a highly educative experience? The answer is yes, but only in the same competitive degree that the campus newspaper is also an educative experience. The pattern is the same in either case; the university glee club could have been employed as an equally realistic medium of expression for the evaluations to be drawn.

No one is more eager than the author to have clearly understood what this book purports to be. It is an effort to re-create from the author's undergraduate years at college—and from those of some of his classmates—the patterns of experience that would have made so clear what he was to have learned by thirds or halves when, perhaps, he could have gained fuller value from the ivy years had he known earlier how to read the signposts with greater accuracy. Essentially this is a book reconstructing four years of college and finding only part of the wisdom obtained coming from classrooms and lecture halls. Through the mind and heart of Jeremy it is the author's story principally, but it is also the story of Iron Man and Creeper and Muggsy and a dozen others—a story of all those little things which, isolated by themselves, may seem trivial, but which brought together should tell a story of buoyant living and hearty growth, albeit from a worm's eye view.

E. S. M.

Rutgers University
New Brunswick, New Jersey
April, 1945

THE IVY YEARS

I

JEREMY

I

Jeremy possessed ten toes and all of them ached. The fuzzy numbness that had been creeping down his leg appeared now to end at the base of his heel, and if he flexed the muscles of his foot he could produce a sensation of needle-points shooting through his veins. He was conscious also of a pinch in the small of his back and of a growing throb between the blades of his shoulders, but neither of these annoyances disturbed him half so much as the fact that it was difficult for him to see, since the shade of a bridge lamp kept swinging down in front of his face and stinging the tip of his nose. But beset though Jeremy seemed on every side—the books on the ledge above the rear seat of the sedan had come untied and with each bounce of the car descended upon the back of his neck—the boy rode on uncomplainingly, his heart light, his head a bit giddy with excitement, his whole being charged with the tingling sweetness of an almost explosive happiness. By a remarkable feat of mental gymnastics Jeremy transported himself away from the world of worrisome reality; in one flying leap of fancy he flung himself completely out of the carcass of the wretch known to humanity as Jeremy Baxter and landed in the skin and bones of the Prodigious Hickey off to school in an Owen Johnson book, or (better yet) into the baggy trousers of a Ralph Henry

Barbour hero speeding back to ivy-covered halls and the convivial life of school away from home. . . .

But at that moment Mr. Baxter slammed on the brakes, the car stopped as though it had run head on into a bulldozer, and Jeremy buried his face in a pile of bed linen. He straightened up cautiously, avoiding the guillotine-like swish of the lamp shade and settling back with a smile of satisfaction at the fact that his abrasions seemed so slight. And then the copy of Wells's *Outline of History* descended with a thwack. Jeremy held his tongue out of deference to his mother, but he thought privately that it served him right, seeing how he was always buying books that he never read anyhow.

When Jeremy had driven away from home less than an hour ago, there had been space in the back of the car for both his feet, but that had been before the two kids in the rusty roadster had tried to beat the red light and Mr. Baxter had driven up over the curb to avoid a collision. Since then Jeremy had been hazy concerning the precise whereabouts of his right foot, save that he believed it was somewhere under the three suitcases, the base of the bridge lamp, and the red lacquered bookrack. Aware suddenly of the bookrack, Jeremy guessed that he liked it. His father had made the thing out of second hand lumber, and if you didn't look too closely you couldn't see where the nail holes had been filled with putty. The bookrack by now had become a Baxter family tradition. Mr. Baxter hadn't wanted to build it, but Mrs. Baxter had wanted him to and had refused to assume any of the responsibility when in a misguided moment Mr. Baxter had pounded his thumb instead of a nail. The gist of Mr. Baxter's remarks, once they had acquired coherence, had been a blankety-blank wish that Jeremy and his mother had never gone to inspect the blankety-blank room where Jeremy was going to live when he went away to college.

Jeremy recalled that journey with mixed emotion. At nineteen he had grown to recognize in his mother the strength of mind that comes to a woman who has raised a family on a house painter's uncertain income and who, if Mr. Baxter could be quoted as a competent authority, could haggle the devil into coming down a notch on his price. Never once had Jeremy denied that a quick wit, resourcefulness, and determination were among his mother's finest virtues; for a moment when they had reached the college and he had seen for the first time the fine old buildings, the shadowed walks, the tall trees, and the lovely lawn of the campus, he had simply forgotten the commonplace realities of previous existence. The janitor of Hegeman Dormitory had not wanted to open the building at four o'clock on a lazy August afternoon, but he had. Morever he had made two patient treks to the basement, once to bring a tape measure so that Mrs. Baxter could determine the length of the window curtains she was making and once to find a stronger bulb for the overhead light; and then after assuring Mrs. Baxter that before her offspring arrived every inch of the room would be scrubbed until it sparkled, the janitor had betrayed Mr. Baxter by agreeing that a bookcase would, indeed, look very nice just under the window. Through all these discussions Jeremy had remained in the background, silent and embarrassed. Sensing his uneasiness, his mother had stopped her deliberations just long enough to say, rather tartly, "Of course, Jeremy, if we were made of money . . ." Jeremy had said nothing, but when the janitor locked the door he had revealed that he understood the cause of the boy's injured dignity.

"Look, Junior," said this wise old gentleman who had seen them come in limousines and jitneys, and some of the best in both, "once you get here you'll change everything around to suit yourself. Mothers like to meddle; it sort of helps 'em forget what a wrench your going away means. I've seen 'em even test the bed springs, but I say God bless mothers; never saw one yet who didn't have her heart in the right place."

In one of those rare interludes when the lamp shade remained stationary, Jeremy glimpsed the fleeting countryside. His mind identified a landmark from his previous journey to the college—the bridge over the railroad cut in Metuchen. In another ten minutes they would reach New Brunswick and the bridge over the Raritan; they would drive down the street along the river and turn at the corner by the rusted gas tank; the climb up the hill by the railroad overpass was drab and depressing, but once they turned under the trestle they would see the campus: the driveway curving up through the ancient trees, the Chapel, Old Queen's that the freshman handbook said had been the heart of the college since 1808. Jeremy, anticipating the moment, once more became the Prodigious Hickey. . . .

And then his glance came back to the red lacquered bookcase. He felt a little ashamed of himself for remembering the nail holes that had been filled with putty. That bookcase was fine. It stood for mom and pop, for all the extra little things they always managed to do—yes, and for the deep affection and the willingness to sacrifice that was the sound, good basis of their occasional squabbles. Somehow they had always succeeded in doing more than he expected; in owning a car even though the seat of pop's trousers was wearing thin; in sending him to college. All summer mom and pop had been talking about his going, planning for it in countless intimate ways—pop saving out of his meager lunch allowance to buy the bridge lamp, mom mending Jeremy's shirts and underwear and squeezing a little out of the budget one week to have his overcoat dry cleaned, a little more next week for his topcoat or a pair of shoes or the radio. His going to college had been important to pop—to pop who all his life had worked with his hands, the hard way, the poor wages way.

And important to mom, too—to mom who on his college entrance application had made him list his father's occupation as "interior decorator," but whose pride wasn't the kind that goeth before a fall but the pride of a stout heart, an uplifted chin. Jeremy wanted suddenly to cry—for all the little privations pop and mom had known all their lives, for the determination they shared that he wasn't going to have to travel the same rocky road. And the tears were even harder to hold back when Jeremy reflected that in another two hours he would be alone—in a strange room, in a strange town.

He was deeply frightened—not only by the first awful constrictions of homesickness, but also by the knowledge that pop and mom were depending so earnestly on college to do so much for him. They were almost childlike in their faith. Education to them was the fount of power. College made you a gentleman. A leader. A better breadwinner. He had heard them say that. College, they believed, opened a door to a fuller, richer life—to a life that wasn't all scrimping and saving and doing without. But did it? Somewhere that summer he had read that the purpose of a college education was to make you know yourself better, to live with yourself more comfortably, to become a better husband and father and friend. Would pop and mom be satisfied with that? The statement had quoted some old Greek—Jeremy had forgotten his name, and didn't know whether he had been a philosopher as all the ancient Greeks seemed to have been, or just a hash-slinger as the only two Greeks Jeremy knew were—who had said that the meaning of all wisdom could be summed up in two words: Know thyself. Jeremy shook his head, worried, perplexed, a bit scared.

Pop said with a chuckle, "If this is your famous Raritan, I'd hate to eat the fish that come out of it."

Jeremy looked down at the roily water and had to agree. "But wait until you see the college," he said. The note of pride in his voice was unmistakable. Already it had become his college.

He was eager again. His mother began to powder her nose. And pop hummed somewhat tonelessly, "There'll be a hot time in the old town tonight." Mom told pop where to turn and Jeremy started watching for the first sight of the trees, the ivy-covered buildings, the others like himself who would be arriving as freshmen. One friend. The homesick feeling would go away, he felt certain, after he had made his first friend.

II

Near by a swarm of sour flies hovered angrily above a discarded apple core. Jeremy sat on the door step of House Four, Hegeman, his arms around his knees, and thought sadly that mom and pop must have reached home by now. Beside him the boy named Joe stirred restlessly.

"I'm glad you got here early," Joe said. "It was sure lonely hanging around by myself."

Jeremy nodded. Down the campus pathway he could see a group approaching: father, mother, son. The trio appeared laden with luggage; even the mother carted a suitcase. The boy's arms had been piled high with bed linen; and his face, ruddy with self-consciousness, was mainly visible because one of the pillows kept falling onto the ground, causing him to stop, set down his entire load, place the pillow back on top, and then struggle to lift it all into his arms. Jeremy grinned with a wicked feeling of complacent superiority; he was settled at college while the boy with the bed linen was not; a wonderful sense of belonging swept over him.

"Why did you come here?" Joe asked.

Jeremy wasn't really sure. The school hadn't been too far away from home, it had seemed as reasonable as any other, and a boy he had known in high school had come here.

"It's a good school," Joe said, almost with a touch of belligerency. "Lots of great guys have gone here."

"Like you and me?"

Joe laughed. Suddenly the barrier of strangeness that had stood between them seemed to disappear. Joe's last name was Bartino and he came from Newark, New Jersey; he had played football three years at Barringer High School and was going to sign up in the morning for the freshman team; he gave the impression, quietly and convincingly, that he intended to be a campus big shot. When Joe paused momentarily, his glance off in the far spaces, Jeremy supposed somewhat enviously that Joe was seeing himself in one of those sweet, heroic autumn afternoons ahead when he would trot out onto the gridiron before the cheering thousands; but Joe's eyes saw the quiet magnificence of the campus, the curve of the river below the red shale bluffs, the gentle roll of the green hills beyond. In his mind Joe recalled the environment that for so long had been home to him: the city street with the rumbling trolleys, the neon-lighted taverns around the corner from his father's printing business, the Monday morning junk heaps by the curb. He shook his head, stirred. College was a big step away; college was a place where a guy could begin to feel like class.

Something about Jeremy disturbed Joe. The kid seemed awfully nervous. Joe didn't know; maybe Jeremy had St. Vitus dance. Joe wanted to ask him what was making him so fidgety, but he didn't know how. He said instead, "It's hot. Let's walk downtown for a soda."

"All right," Jeremy said. He knew that Joe was watching him rather sharply and was glad to get up.

They reached College Avenue, and across the street on the porch of the Chi Psi house two seniors were talking to a girl in a wide-brimmed white hat. Joe tried to catch the girl's glance and to make her smile, but there wasn't even a tumble.

Jeremy walked on, not even noticing that Joe still tried to attract the girl's attention. Jeremy was thinking about his affliction. Of course he had to expect Joe to become conscious of it; everybody did sooner or later. It wasn't something he could hide very easily, although his first impluse was to try. Really there wasn't much about his handicap that he could explain beyond the fact that it was an infernal nuisance, and anybody could observe that. His hands and arms were seized occasionally with involuntary tremors, that's all there was to it; he had been troubled this way ever since he could remember, and an injury to the back of his brain at birth had been the cause. Naturally the affliction made him sensitive when he was reminded of it, but it made him stubborn, too. To hell with anybody who thought he couldn't get along.

"That girl had a nice build," Joe said wistfully.

Jeremy came out of his reverie, but they were too far beyond the Chi Psi porch for him to see now. Across from the main campus on Somerset Street they discovered Louie's—one of those little eating places with too many pennants and menus printed in purple duplicator ink that came off on your fingers. At the border between town and gown in every college community Jeremy suspected that there was a Louie's—and a Mrs. Louie too, middle-aged, big-bosomed and big-hearted, with a kind, homely face and mouse-brown hair. Mrs. Louie brought their sodas and Jeremy asked for a straw.

"Chust a minute, dollink," Mrs. Louie said. From the rear, when she walked, the woman resembled Donald Duck. Jeremy wanted to laugh. In another moment she returned, empty-handed and apologetic. "Dollink, we ain't got no more straws."

It was like turning a corner, Jeremy thought, and finding that the street ended for no sensible reason against a stone wall. Without a straw he was helpless. If he tried to pick up the glass, his nerves would betray him; he'd be lucky if half of the soda didn't splash onto Joe.

Mrs. Louie's eyes were filled with understanding. "Dollink, let me hold it for you."

Jeremy nodded. He hated being made conspicuous. It was like being an infant in long trousers; he felt like a fool. Not sorry for himself, but wishing he could have managed it alone. Unhappy, but not so much so that the soda didn't taste good.

"Next time we have straws," Mrs. Louie said.

Joe said, "Look, when we go to the college cafeteria tonight maybe they won't have any straws either. You sit by me."

Jeremy, looking up, saw that Joe's big broad face was clean and youthful and attractive.

Walking back to Hegeman, Jeremy told Joe about his affliction. He tried to make his experiences sound funny and amusing, for they were easier to tell that way. As Joe could understand, it was difficult for him to write with pen or pencil and so he had carted a typewriter from class to class in high school; everybody grew accustomed to his typing, except his Spanish teacher who jerked her head around whenever the bell on the carriage of the typewriter rang at the end of a line.

"Funny part of it was, Joe, she wore a wig, and when her head came up quick you could see it bounce. She passed me to save her dignity."

Joe chuckled; it was a good story even if Jeremy had invented it. But some of the things that Jeremy's affliction had meant to a kid growing up couldn't be made to sound light-hearted. A doctor's office, the waiting room of a clinic, a hospital examination room with doctors and internes and student nurses all grouped around—those things told as they were lived, dully, a note of heartbreak underneath because there were always more. And then one day in a city clinic Jeremy had encountered an old German doctor who had refused to examine him.

"Joe, that doctor just took one look at my record and

turned on mom as though he was going to blow his top—and maybe hers too. 'Get this boy out of hospitals,' he said with that tone Prussians use when you can hear them a block away. 'This boy needs nothing but education . . . all the education you can give him . . . education and nothing more!' "

Joe never forgot the story. Through all the ivy years whenever he thought of Jeremy he thought of the Prussian doctor. He thought of him, too, whenever he met blind Carl Becker, who followed a Seeing Eye dog from class to class, or Gordy McLean, a victim of infantile paralysis who walked on crutches and waited patiently at the bottom of every flight of stairs until some classmate or professor came along and offered to carry Gordy the remainder of the way.

When Joe went home for the Christmas holidays, he told his mother the story, and about Carl and Gordy. His mother's eyes dimmed, but Joe couldn't understand why. All those guys seemed to get along all right. By then Joe had won no small place for himself on the campus, and nobody ever thought to call him Joe any more—not after that day at football practice when Joe had sent one varsity tackle to the infirmary with a cracked skull and a dozen other varsity linemen back to the showers with a ruffled dignity. After that solemn afternoon Joe sometimes was called Wildcat, sometimes the Newark Nemesis, but more often Iron Man.

III

Jeremy and Muggsy met for the first time the evening following their arrival at college—two naked figures groping through the steam from the showers in quest of the same cake of soap. Soberly they shook hands, Muggsy perhaps the more sober of the pair for there was a touch of pathos in the bulge of his pot-like little stomach. Muggsy leaned against the window sill, a towel around his loins, and like an overgrown Buddha gazed down at his navel.

"It never grew in," he said dismally.

"Does it matter?"

"I'd like my belly button to grow in," Muggsy said defiantly. "It's only right that it should!"

Jeremy couldn't hold back a chuckle. Something about Muggsy marked him at first meeting as a lovable clown. Muggsy's real name was Porter Lippincott; and he had grown up in a splendid, century-old home in Monmouth County, New Jersey, where on an early spring morning as he lay in a hand-pegged cherry bed he could hear the crows and catbirds cawing in the marsh grass around Little Silver Inlet. In House Four, Hegeman, Muggsy occupied the room directly above Iron Man, but where Iron Man became distinguished almost at once as one of the future stalwarts of the varsity eleven, Muggsy's first claim to notoriety came as a member of the college band when, marching onto the field at the opening football game, he turned the wrong way and so stood alone for ten dreadful seconds—a tall, ungainly, stoop-shouldered boy tooting a clarinet with myopic concentration. That Muggsy should live directly across from the one lavatory in House Four and still should keep under his bed the only chamber of convenience in the college (which he claimed once had belonged to his grandmother and therefore possessed "sentimental attachments") was simply typical of Muggsy; and it was typical, too, that Muggsy should fight like an infuriated banshee on the evening when Iron Man, having collected lighter fluid from every occupant in Hegeman, snatched the chamber and set the whole mess ablaze while sitting on the abdomen of a puff-depleted Muggsy. The heat of the fire scorched Iron Man's hands, the vessel crashed in a hundred fragments upon the floor, and Muggsy wept for the inglorious end of a Lippincott heirloom. Iron Man hooted derisively at any family that symbolized the pride of its heritage in an object so utilitarian, but underneath Iron Man was shaken; when he looked at the top of Muggsy's dresser and beheld there bottles of more different kinds of medicine than it is customary to see displayed in a modern drug store he could understand how dearly and how tenderly this only child had been coddled; but the only thing in all his life Iron Man ever coddled was an egg, and then for only three minutes. Even at their first meeting in the steam-filled showers of Hegeman an intuitive voice whispered to Jeremy that wherever he found Muggsy there also he would encounter laughter and fun; and Muggsy, still the forlorn Buddha, took another hitch in the towel around his loins and laughed.

"Have you met Visch?"

"Who's Visch?"

"The junior who lives over me on the third floor. You must have heard Visch even if you haven't seen him. He's the one who plays the mandolin."

Iron Man and Muggsy Jeremy already accepted as among his close friends, and Visch he accepted by proxy. Muggsy clutched his towel and led the way up the stairs to the third floor. There was more vigor than melody to the sound of the mandolin.

The engraved card on the door gave the full name of its proprietor as S. Robert Vischer. Garbed in only his shorts, Visch sat with his feet propped against the window sill; a frail boy with spindley arms and legs, he resembled a spider attempting to work up the energy to weave a web on which to disport itself.

"Hi," said Muggsy.

"A brilliant conversation."

"He thinks he's that sour-pussed guy in the movies," Muggsy told Jeremy. "You know, Ned Sparks."

"So you brought a friend," the mandolin player said. "Has he got a sister?"

"Why do you think we're friends?"

"You! With a belly like that? By the way, you both owe me a dollar for your campus dues."

"Don't pay it," Muggsy said. "That's a gag so old they tried it on my dad when he went to Princeton. He paid it, the sap. And probably to some unprincipled crook like you —a junior from *Brooklyn*."

"Nice town, Brooklyn," Visch said. "Some day they'll annex it to the United States."

Jeremy, who would have paid the dollar for the fictitious campus dues if Muggsy hadn't warned him, liked Visch nonetheless—and liked him more the better he knew him. Visch's frailness of physique was, in a sense, his heartbreak; Jeremy had not lived with a handicap all his life not to understand that a sharp wit was a natural shield against the world. Anyone who knew Visch for an hour learned that the Brooklyn boy was consumed with the will to be a dentist. Visch already had spent a year at the Columbia Dental School and had been discharged on the grounds that it was doubtful if he possesssed sufficient strength for making an extraction; now he had come back to Rutgers principally to pass another year until he could apply for readmission to Columbia. For a time Visch was the center of a mystery in House Four. Twice a week the junior would be gone from his room and nobody would know where or why; but in time Muggsy sweated the truth out of him—Visch was attending vocational night school in Perth Amboy, learning to work on a lathe and thus developing digital dexterity in the making of a large scale set of dental drills, all in the desperately earnest hope that this performance would convince the authorities at Columbia that he could be a dentist. Somehow this slim-built, sober-eyed youngster whose ribs had a tendency now and then of poking through his undershirt brought an unconsciously acknowledged ache into House Four. Jeremy felt it acutely. Like Muggsy and Iron Man he wanted Visch to become the dentist he dreamed of being, and yet he could not be sure that Visch would. And if Visch could fail in his fondest dream, then why couldn't he or Iron Man or Muggsy? The uneasiness that Visch symbolized was all the more frightening at times, for Visch was so willing to work and sweat and sacrifice to achieve his goal. Willingness and ambition *without* ability—these could create deep and lasting heartbreak. More than once, trying to fall asleep, Jeremy would stare up at the ceiling where the street light on Bishop Place cast a silver streak. He had his own handicap to face. If the ivy years were to bring him up against this same grim reality, was he man enough to take it?

Even more than Muggsy or Iron Man, Visch became Jeremy's confidant. He didn't mind if Visch were sarcastic; Jeremy could be sharp-tongued himself at times, and much in the same mechanistic spirit of self-defense. They shared opinions on everything, another way of saying they liked to argue. And deep differences of viewpoint cropped up between them; the Negro question, kindled into white heat on the evening in the college cafeteria when Visch refused to sit at the table with the one Negro boy in Jeremy's class, caused them to part in bitterness.

"You're an intolerant slob," Jeremy charged, for once getting the jump on Visch in name-calling.

"And you are an empty-headed, Nigger-loving, fool socialist," Visch retorted, his tone mean-tempered.

Jeremy's cheeks were flushed. "I'll tell you one thing. I'd rather be a well-to-do socialist than a down-at-the-heel capitalist!"

No argument could surmount so Chestertonian a paradox.

Actually Visch created the impression that his family was easily as well-off and as socially prominent as Muggsy's. Jeremy harbored a disappointment at the fact that he was never invited to go home with Visch for a week end, and once, visiting in New York City during a college vacation,

Jeremy decided on impulse to ride the subway to Brooklyn. He came out of the underground into the bright glare of a frosty day to find himself but a few blocks from Visch's home. Aristocratic brownstone houses lined the street, and Jeremy decided that here was a neighborhood where the best Brooklyn families had lived for generations. But a block from the subway station a Negro ran the corner drug store; two Negroes waited at the counter in a butcher shop half way down the block; a Negro boy came howling out the front door of one of the brownstone houses across the street. Jeremy's own family lived near enough to the bare subsistence level for him to realize how deep ran the prejudice against Negroes who came into white neighborhoods where rent was already a sizable item, and the torment and expense of moving was more acute because with moving came a sense of enforced uprooting, of flight from one temporary haven to the next. Standing in the glare of the noonday sun, Jeremy saw a visit to Visch's home as an intrusion. He turned back to the subway station.

In his first letter home Jeremy wrote his mother with unconcealed jubilation: "I've made three good friends already; don't worry, I'm going to get along all right." For the most part the dwellers in Hegeman who had but slight contact with Jeremy's own intimate circle disturbed him very little; he knew them all by name within a week. As a rule the aggies were most congenial with other aggies, the premedics with other premedics. And with some birds, even if you could see their plumage you wondered how they had learned to fly. Bob Imbrie was in that class; Visch quoted odds of five to one that this specimen wouldn't last the term. Bob was devoured with a passion for acquiring all of the little five-cent blue books published by the Haldeman-Julius Company in Girard, Kansas; he read them avidly, to the complete neglect of his textbooks. In a way he was the most erudite undergraduate in the college, equally at ease quoting Plato or

Ingersoll, the Bible or the Koran, Shakespeare or Thomas Aquinas; he knew by heart ninety sample love letters, all guaranteed to produce results, but none of his professors ever examined him on this fascinating subject. And there was a sullen boy on the first floor who lived a mole-like existence behind a closed door and was never encountered except in the showers where, to the infuriation of his house-mates, he made a great fuss of spreading newspapers on the floor before walking in his bare feet where the others had walked. He never picked up the newspapers, either; they became the mark by which Jeremy knew he still existed. And there was a Scudder—there always had been Scudders at the college—a nice boy, pleasant-mannered and quiet-spoken, who spent most of his time at his fraternity house. But Jeremy was happy with his own crowd; the fear of the strange room in a strange town, like so many of the fears of youth, had quickly dissolved.

IV

Jeremy admitted that he had harbored a number of fool-ish notions about what coming to college would be like. He had believed that a group of upperclassmen would drop by and give him a word of friendly advice, but apparently up-perclassmen lived by themselves among the clouds. In the best Ralph Henry Barbour tradition he had expected the sophomores to descend in a body and a brawl to ensue, but nobody offered to tar and feather him. The ivy years simply began, anticlimactic though that fact seemed; Jeremy arrived on a Sunday afternoon and the janitor, stiff and uncomfort-able in his best blue serge suit, unlocked the door to his room; and then on Monday morning he rushed through breakfast so that at ten minutes to nine he could report at the chapel for the beginning of a four-day orientation period. The chapel meeting opened with an address by the president of the university, who exhorted the young hopefuls to apply themselves; a fat dean and a skinny dean mounted the rostrum to say much the same thing; and a prominent alumnus who had done well in business arose to proclaim that the old world was obviously going to pot and that unless their generation saved it heaven only knew what could. This was all good, sound, unimaginative advice, and Jeremy was inclined to believe Visch's dour observation that the pattern of greeting hadn't varied a great deal since Harvard had set up for business at Cambridge in 1636. Muggsy and Jeremy watched Iron Man carving his initials into a chapel pew while they were being harangued; then they stumbled back into the late September sunlight, ate a greasy meal in Louie's, and trudged over to the gymnasium for a three-hour English placement examination. Exhausted and befuddled, they went back to Hegeman, each cheering the other with the assurance that they hadn't done so badly as they feared; the morrow offered them little relief for in the morning they would be herded into the gymnasium for a physical examination and then for another three-hour grind, this time to test their intelligence so that they could be safely stamped as "college material"; but with all their suspected shortcomings a sense of exuberance persisted. They were in college. Officially.

On the last evening of the orientation period Jeremy went down to the gym for a rally of the entire student body. The purpose of the meeting was to introduce the freshmen to the current crop of campus heroes—the president of Student Council, the cheerleaders, the editor of the campus newspaper, the members of the varsity football squad—and Iron Man's eyes glowed with anticipation for the years ahead when he could be one of those awesome personages on the platform. Afterward the freshmen were taught the college cheers and songs, and then a gray-haired man with a quiet, gentle voice told the group about the traditions of the university. His name was Earl Reed Silvers, and everybody liked his speech, for it was like something out of a book.

Muggsy and Jeremy looked around for Iron Man after the meeting, but he had gone off with a group of upper-classmen, men from the varsity eleven.

"Iron Man's being rushed by the fraternities," Muggsy said.

"Iron Man's going to make out all right," Jeremy answered rather enviously.

They walked along in silence under the tall, dark trees, and then Muggsy said, "I'm going to have dinner with the Lambda Chis tomorrow night."

Jeremy didn't say much; because his affliction sometimes made him feel an ugly duckling socially, he wanted to be accepted socially; there were moments when the yearning was deep in his bones and twisted his sense of proportion; and when such moments seized him, the social acceptance that went with receiving a bid to a fraternity could seem little less than life or death to him. Some of the frustrations that had dogged his youth returned to haunt the walk back to Hegeman; he remembered little incidents that had seemed so trivial at the moment and yet apparently had lingered in his mind like hidden wounds ready to itch and burn with every change of temperature—the morbid curiosity of some thoughtless old man asking how long he had been troubled with the shakes; the laughter one day when he had dropped a tray in the high school cafeteria; the girls he had wanted to ask to dances and hadn't because of the painful shyness his affliction had nurtured.

"Rubbish!" his mind said, but not his heart. Fraternities meant something: in the evening when the members of fra-ternity rushing committees were going through the dor-mitories, looking for a freshman here or there to invite to dinner and maybe send back that night proudly wearing a pledge pin, it was natural to hope that he'd be next—a knock on the door, a cordial greeting, laughter and hand-shakes and a personal invitation, more laughter, an eager acceptance, and a dash up to the showers to shave and to comb his hair before going over to the chapter house. A rushing period was exciting, something everyone talked about almost as much as football.

Jeremy's moroseness grew on him; when they reached Hegeman he muttered good night to Muggsy and climbed the stairs to his own room wearing his gloom like a cape around his shoulders. He wanted to nourish his misery in privacy, but Visch's thin, sharp nose edged through the door and the mandolin twanged discordantly.

"Who kicked you in the teeth?"

"My grandmother."

"What did she play at Vassar?"

"She mended the bloomers back in the huddle."

Visch started to laugh, then stopped. His tone was surprisingly gentle. "What's eating you, kid?"

Jeremy told him.

"Isn't that mostly self-pity?"

"Is it?"

"Yes, it is. Somebody's told you misery has to have company, but that's bunk. Nobody likes a cry baby—not even a nervous one."

"Who says I'm a cry baby?"

"I do. Another thing, don't try to take out your grudge against society on Muggsy. Let him join a fraternity if he wants to. Muggsy's nobody's fool, except on the surface. He'll still be your friend, no matter where he goes, but don't try to bolster your ego by thinking that if the fraternities don't want you they won't want Muggsy."

"They can have Muggsy. They can have you, too. Now let me go to bed."

"You're a sap," Visch said. "Why do you think a fraternity is such a sacred cow? Don't you know there're a lot of Joes in fraternities who wish they weren't? Joining a fraternity just because it seems fashionable is rot. All right, a

guy goes into a house to live for three or four years. Unless
he has much in common with the other guys in the house,
how's it going to work? Joining a fraternity is a serious step;
get in the wrong crowd and it's pretty awful, let me tell you.
Sure, there are good houses, but there are bad ones, and a
sensitive kid like yourself is better out than in one of those!"

Jeremy began unbuttoning his shirt, but now he wasn't
so eager for Visch to leave. "Any houses rush you?"

"The Dekes and the Phi Gams."

"Why didn't you join?"

"I'd join the Phi Gams if I weren't going back to Columbia next year, but I wouldn't do it to satisfy my ego. I'd
join because I like the idea of eating my meals with the
same group under conditions that are closer to those at
home. I'd do it because there's a house committee to take
care of ill-bred young asses who spread newspapers all over
the shower room floor. I'd do it because it's a nice way to live
at college—in a home, with the little touches that go with
cultured living. I'd do it because there's a prescribed study
period and a community spirit of leadership and a place to
bring a girl for a party week end. But I'm not going to join
and I'm not going to be down in the mouth about it—and
neither are you!"

Jeremy took off his shirt and hung it on the back of the
desk chair. "I've got a couple of apples around somewhere.
Want one?"

"You had a couple. But I left you one. I didn't like the
look of the worm hole in it.". . .

One night about a week later Jeremy fell asleep while
studying in Visch's room, and it was nearly one in the morning when he awoke. Visch sat at his desk, watching him.

"Why didn't you kick me out?"

Visch looked a trifle sheepish. "I had a stop watch on you.
When you were awake and studying those involuntary
tremors came about once every three or four minutes. When

you were sleeping they came once every thirty or forty minutes. I guess that only means you can lick that thing as long
as you can keep relaxed. Maybe it'll help some day, knowing
that."

Jeremy didn't know what to say. Visch had sat for three
hours, watching. Out of friendship. Because he believed
there was a solution to Jeremy's problem more important
than joining a fraternity. At times the experience of young
men living intimately together produced nettlesome impulses, but at other times a rough, affectionate camaraderie
came to the surface. Perhaps tenderness was almost the word.

JEREMY

2

THE BITTER AND THE SWEET

I

Jeremy couldn't put off any longer going to see his faculty adviser. Muggsy, always more punctilious in meeting such obligations, had called on Allen Sinclair Will two weeks ago but Jeremy had neglected from day to day his meeting with Dr. Will because his afternoons were filled with other divertissements: the movies, sitting in the bleachers at Neilson Field and watching Iron Man lose ten pounds scrimmaging against the varsity, or playing touch football on a weedy, unromanticized field where on a windy November afternoon in 1869 twenty-five undergraduates from Princeton had opposed twenty-five undergraduates from Rutgers in America's first game of intercollegiate football. But one morning in Jeremy's mail box there was a letter from his faculty adviser that said rather ominously:

> *If you wish to continue as a student in journalism kindly see me before four o'clock this afternoon.*

As Jeremy charged down College Avenue, he reckoned that he would meet the appointment with a minute to spare. As Muggsy said, all that Dr. Will could do was to check over the courses Jeremy was taking, and that seemed a waste of time since on registration day Marvin, dean of the College of Arts and Sciences, had humphed and hawed over Jeremy's class schedule and had found the correct courses listed—English, algebra, history, German (in preference to Italian, French, Spanish, Latin, or Greek), geology (in preference to physics or chemistry), and physical education in place of military science.

Dr. Will was just reaching for his hat when Jeremy burst into the office. Panting from a last minute sprint up the flight of stairs that led to the quarters of the department of journalism, Jeremy looked into the somewhat startled face of an elderly man whose white hair and rather florid complexion gave him the appearance of prim and adequately nourished dignity.

"If you're rushing for the 4:15 express to New York, you're three blocks from the station."

"I'm sorry if I'm late, sir."

"About three weeks late, as a matter of fact."

"I'm sorry, sir."

"Punctuality is one of the cardinal rules of newspaper work."

"Yes, sir!"

"Suppose you had a job on *The New York Times* and you were assigned an important story and then neglected to bring it in until after it had been published in all the other papers for three weeks, what do you think your editor would say?"

"I think he'd question the legitimacy of my birth, sir."

Will's mouth drew tighter. "Mr. Baxter, precisely why did you choose journalism for your major?"

Jeremy began to breathe more easily. As a future member of the fourth estate he possibly claimed more than the normal quota of conceit for a lad who still shaved more out of vanity than necessity. First as the author at ten cents a column inch of yard after yard of high school notes for his home town newspaper, then as summer reporter on space rates for two weeklies, Jeremy had succeeded in two years in accumulating twelve hundred dollars toward his college expenses. Without this nest egg college might well have been out of the question for the son of a house painter, and Jeremy took an honest pride in his accomplishment.

For a moment Will's eyes softened, and there was warmth in his smile. Jeremy was instantly disarmed, for once the old man surrendered his pose of pompousness and ceased talking like a collection of animated mottoes he seemed likable and human.

"Of course," Will said, "there's more to newspaper work than writing stories at home on space rates."

"I know that, sir."

"On the copydesk a man has to be able to edit rapidly and write his slug lines and heads in pencil."

"Or on a typewriter, sir."

"That would be rather difficult. And on the rewrite desk —or even out covering a story as a leg man—a man has to take notes."

Jeremy suddenly felt flustered, for obviously Will was trying to tell him that his affliction made him ill-suited for newspaper work. A tightness crept into Jeremy's heart, a leaden feeling of frustration, bitterness, and resentment. His voice was thin-edged with stubbornness. "Dean Marvin has accepted me as a candidate for a degree in journalism."

"I am head of the department," Will retorted, his dignity seeming to rise up like the fur on the back of an angry cat.

"I'll make out all right," Jeremy said, scared by this unexpected threat to all his dreams. "I'm able to take care of myself. I came to college to get an education in journalism, sir, because that's what I'm best at."

The faculty adviser could not mistake the note of pleading in the boy's voice. He felt saddened and defeated. He had given his life to newspaper work as an editor on *The Baltimore Sun, The Philadelphia North American,* and *The New York Times,* and he knew. This boy wouldn't fit. Again, the man thought of the record he had made at the university

—never a student graduated who had not been placed in newspaper work. This boy would break the record.

Dr. Will looked down into the storminess of Jeremy's eyes determined to face the truth, then lost his nerve. "Well, there's no need to worry until your junior year when you take your professional courses. Perhaps your physical condition will have improved by then. I'm glad you came in."

"Thank you, sir." But there was an unmistakable stiffness in Jeremy's manner; he slammed the door going out. An old fear nipped at his heels as he stomped down the stairs; he couldn't elude it forever. The old German doctor could have been wrong. College and education might not make enough difference. The boy was shaken and frightened; he wanted to run away from the thought of his handicap, but Will had thrown the salt of doubt upon the deep wound of his own secret misgiving.

Jeremy hated the man. At the corner he stopped and looked back at the ivy-covered building where journalism was taught. In his eyes Will had become the embodiment of the ogre who so often haunted the dark corners of his mind—that unidentifiable rascal who made moments of solitude so terrifying with his wretched whispering: "You can't . . . you won't . . . you'll never do it!" Jeremy raised his fist and shook it, mostly to force back the tears. He said aloud:

"Damn him!"

Jeremy's confidence remained deeply shaken. He trudged back along College Avenue, muttering angrily to himself, kicking viciously at a stone that appeared in his way. Will wasn't going to throw him out of journalism—no, damn his fat old head, not if he had to take the case to the president! Suppose he couldn't take notes—he could see and feel and remember. What was more he could write—maybe better than old Will himself. Let them try to keep him out of journalism, just let them try! He'd raise a stink, by damn

—a stink that would be in every newspaper in the east. Since when had education become the privilege of only the physically perfect? For a moment Jeremy saw himself in imaginary headlines, a martyr and a hero, and the thought of how he would crush Will and bring the whole college to shame was alluring. But the moment passed swiftly; he was plain Jeremy Baxter again, a guy with the shakes who maybe didn't belong in journalism. Maybe he didn't belong anywhere. He knew that self-pity was warping his perspective, and he didn't care. And he wasn't going to take it. No, by damn, not from Will or the college or anybody. They'd give him the education he wanted. He was paying the bills, and as long as he could pay them nobody was kicking him around.

Muggsy and Visch were playing cribbage when Jeremy reached Hegeman. The game stopped; Jeremy was too full of anger and heartbreak to keep the Will interview to himself.

"That was a lousy way to act," Visch said indignantly. "I don't know how birds like that ever get on a college faculty."

"Nuts to Will," Muggsy said.

Jeremy's eyes were blinking, his nerves tight. Visch's and Muggsy's loyalty only seemed to undermine his emotional control; he felt all choked up, ready to explode, and if Will could see him now the man would know that he had been right. The newspaper business was a hard-boiled racket. It hadn't been designed for kids who wanted to cry when somebody slapped them hard. Maybe Will wasn't such a fool at heart; maybe he was only being fair, laying all the cards on the table, as the authorities at Columbia had done with Visch. But Jeremy wouldn't give in to the small, thin voice of reason trying to whisper to his conscience. He hated Will; he wasn't going to back down to him now or ever.

"Listen," Muggsy said, "you've simply got to laugh at lugs like that. Listen, I made up a limerick about Will—

> *"There once was a Prof named Will*
> *Who chased a dame up a hill*
> *When they got to the top*
> *They both came to a stop*
> *And—"*

"What's the rest of it?" Visch asked with a Rabelaisian eagerness.

Muggsy laughed. "You think it's going to be dirty, but it's not—

> *"And they danced a clumsy quadrille."*

Jeremy's smile was crooked and uncertain. He turned, went into his room, and closed the door. Then he flung himself on the bed and buried his head in his arms. He couldn't cry, and he wanted to. When he was choked up this way, he sometimes thought that he'd just as soon be dead. But in his heart he knew that he was acting like a child giving way to such silly thoughts. Why had he expected Dr. Will to coddle him? Had the man spoken anything more than the truth—that he was quite obviously afflicted and the handicap would stand against him in newspaper work? Jeremy rolled over on the bed and tried to think sensibly. College was different from any experience he ever had known. Whether he made friends, whether Will permitted him to major in journalism, whether he was accepted by a fraternity—each was his problem, and how he managed to work his way out of each would, in the end, contribute to the result called *his* education. Jeremy thought, "I won't write mom about this." The temptation was strong to pour out all the misgivings of his heart in a letter home, to know mom would be quickly indignant and loyally sympathetic, but what good would it do? This thing was something out of mom's control. It was something he had to grow up to or bust in the effort. Down the hall Visch began playing his mandolin and Jeremy, listening, tried to forget about himself.

II

By morning Jeremy had regained his sense of humor, and his streak of obstinacy as far as Will was concerned. He didn't have to wait until his junior year to prove he belonged in journalism; the home town newspaper that had printed the high school notes which he had produced so voluminously had appointed him its university correspondent. Since *The Bergen Evening Record* covered one of the most populous counties in the state, Jeremy could record the college activities of students from some thirty communities; and with his rate raised to fifteen cents a column inch he could earn five or six dollars a week. Determined to prove Will wrong through his *Record* stories, Jeremy set out to become the college newshound. And that was how he came to know Earl Reed Silvers.

Professor Silvers's title at the university was director of public relations, a dignified term in academic circles for what the theatrical world calls a press agent. He had come to the college as a freshman in 1909, and had liked the campus so well that he had settled down for life. There was a lithe wiriness about the man, giving credence to the story that as an undergraduate he had been the best miler in the college; there was a warmth and gentleness in his eyes that instantly put Jeremy at ease.

Standing in the doorway to Silvers's office, his freshman dink twisted awkwardly in his hand, Jeremy said, "I'm the correspondent for *The Bergen Evening Record*. I'd like to receive the news releases from this office if I may, sir."

"I've read your copy," the man said. "It's good."

Jeremy's heart lifted.

"And I've heard about you. You're the young scamp who made Will miss the 4:15 to New York the other day."

"Yes, sir," Jeremy admitted. "I'm the scamp."

"Rather told the old boy off, didn't you?"

Jeremy's grin was a trifle tentative. But like most boys and dogs Jeremy possessed a gift for smelling out his friends in a short time. In this first meeting he recognized that there was an unspoken pact between them concerning Will.

"Come in and sit down," Professor Silvers said. "Sit over on this side—by my good ear—and tell me about yourself."

Jeremy saw then that Professor Silvers wore an earphone. Something about the directness with which the man acknowledged his handicap impressed Jeremy in a way that he couldn't identify. He forgot the fact momentarily as he began to talk about himself, and Professor Silvers, sucking on a charred and wheezing corncob pipe, listened quietly. Jeremy rambled on, not pretentiously, for it seemed natural to tell this man the truth: about his father's being a house painter, about how except for his twelve hundred dollars he had come to college more or less on a shoestring, about the old German doctor whose remark had made him desperately aware of how much an education could mean.

"The Will incident hit you pretty hard, didn't it?"

Jeremy nodded.

"Made you want to hit back?"

"Good and hard."

The man smiled. "Perhaps that's part of your education. You're going to be knocked around in life—and knocked down sometimes. But keep getting up. Keep being stronger than anyone who tries to defeat you, no matter what their motives may be."

"Can Will keep me from being a journalist?"

"I don't think he will."

"But can he?"

Silvers shook his head. "Not you, Jeremy. I know he can't. Will is a good teacher, an honest teacher; and having heard his opinions about press agents, I still say so."

"But why can't he stop me, sir?"

"Because you're you, Jeremy. You rule your own destiny; you'll be exactly what you make up your mind to be."

Jeremy desperately wanted to believe so, but the wounds of his confidence were still only partially healed. And yet Silvers had him believing that the way ahead was neither too steep nor too grim; he started to say so when the man behind the desk interrupted him:

"My ears are going back on me. As soon as I put a new battery in this thing everything'll be all right."

Jeremy recognized, if only vaguely, the wisdom Professor Silvers was revealing to him—the wisdom of accepting a handicap with good humor and an unembittered heart. Later, when he thought back over their meeting, he realized that there were two kinds of handicapped persons—those who imposed their afflictions on others by demanding special attention, and those who accepted their situations graciously and put those who would help them at ease to help them. Jeremy kept turning the thought over and over in his mind. Suppose a man were partially deaf or lame or blind or nervous? If he accepted it the world would accept it. The affliction needn't be made so important. But the solution wasn't so easy as it sounded, and Jeremy wasn't fool enough to think that it was. Habit was a deep-rooted, treacherous thing; he had built up defenses against the world—foolish defenses perhaps—but still they were there. If he were lucky, some day he'd outgrow them. And knowing Silvers, sharing his friendship, was going to make it easier to grow away from them. Jeremy clung tenaciously to his hunches. The old German doctor had been a hunch. And Silvers was the same type of hunch. He had won a real ally; he stopped worrying about Will.

Before a fortnight had passed Jeremy became a daily visitor to the office of the Director of Public Relations. Jeremy suspected that he was making a pest of himself, but he kept coming—doggedly, sometimes a little worriedly, for he wondered if Professor Silvers did not experience moments when he shuddered at the sound of his persistent feet pounding up the stairs. But no matter how busy Professor Silvers appeared to be, he always found time for Jeremy. The man never once failed to receive the freshman graciously whether for only five minutes snatched from a busy schedule or for an hour's rambling conversation. If Jeremy had nothing more to recommend him, he was a boy; and for Earl Reed Silvers the ivy years were filled with boys growing up—pesky boys included.

As the days went by Professor Silvers became a personality to Jeremy. He was that happy kind of man whose friendship wore exceedingly well, for he liked the things that mark a man as constant in his affections—odd coats, the same blackened pipes, an oft-repeated story about the college or a friend. His greatest virtue was his loyalty, a loyalty that attached more significance to people than to ideas. It was perhaps a certain indication of enduring friendship that Jeremy made no effort to deny those traits that set aside Professor Silvers as a human being, and he may have tried at times to find them, since in the end they appeared only to strengthen his basic liking for the man. He believed that Silvers liked him more because Will liked him less, and that Silvers's pride had been deeply hurt by Will's disparaging attitude toward publicity men. Such weaknesses in the man's armor as Jeremy discovered, or thought he discovered, did not mean anything in the final accounting; the fact remained that undergraduates seeking advice had been climbing the stairs to Professor Silvers's office for the better part of a quarter of a century.

"Why do you bother with us?" Jeremy asked one day. "Guys like me must clutter up your whole day."

Professor Silvers's eyes, stealing out the window past the maple trees already dropping their yellowed leaves, seemed to possess a sudden far-away look.

"I had a son who died," he said at last. "His name was Terrill, and he was such a bright, handsome little youngster that I knew in the way that fathers know that that boy would have made a good man. Somehow I couldn't quite accept the fact that death had to be final as far as Terrill and I were concerned. I told myself that Terrill still lived if only I had the sense to search for him—in some other lad's eyes, in some other lad's smile, in some other lad's goodness of spirit. And so here on the campus during the past quarter of a century I have played this little game of seeking Terrill—of seeking him and finding him."

Jeremy rubbed his nose, a bit embarrassed. He couldn't trust himself to speak for the moment. The man was an incurable sentimentalist. People were his interest in life, and he delighted in peeping into their hearts, not as an annoying intruder, but as one who came to share the intimacy of their laughter and tears.

"Silvers is all right," Muggsy said when he heard the story. "More guys like that around here and you'd have a real college."

Jeremy nodded. Of such stuff, he was convinced, were educators made.

III

The college was in the throes of an expiring, unsuccessful football season. Major games already had been lost to Syracuse, Holy Cross, and Lafayette, and these discouragements only seemed to substantiate the forebodings that had crept into every heart when Rutgers had opened the season by being ignominiously defeated by Providence College.

"That little dump hasn't more than a couple of hundred students," Visch fumed. "It's a good thing we aren't playing one of those dinky Pennsylvania teacher's colleges or we'd never be able to live it down!"

Jeremy groaned. On the coming Saturday Rutgers would close its season against N.Y.U. at Yankee Stadium. It would be a massacre!

Iron Man alone remained stout-hearted. "You can't tell. If our guards hold up we can win."

"Nuts," Visch sneered.

"I don't see you out for the team."

"I'm saving myself," Visch answered. "For some place where I can do some good—the junior prom."

"We need a new coach," Muggsy flustered. Only nine out of ten disgruntled undergraduates had been circulating this threatening opinion since the Providence debacle eight weeks before.

Iron Man's scowl could not have dropped much lower without brushing his shoe tops. "Rocky's a good coach. You birds shoot off your big mouths about needing a new coach, but you don't know anything about football. Look at the lousy material he's had to work with. We had better backs at Barringer High School."

"We ought to go out and buy a good team," Visch said.

"Yeah," Iron Man said. "Like they do at some schools we play. Those babies put cash on the line."

Jeremy ignored Iron Man's defense of the head coach when he sat down to pound out his midweekly sports story for *The Bergen Evening Record*. He wrote a story that looked good for a column—$4.65 in space rates—about how dissatisfaction was growing over Rocky's coaching and unless Rutgers held N.Y.U. to a close margin the end might be near for Rocky. Reading it over Jeremy had to admit that for a dish of pure conjecture he had created an enticing concoction. He mailed the story on his way down to supper.

With three days remaining before the N.Y.U. game Jeremy abandoned any pretense of studying. Football was all anyone talked—between classes, at meals, during the long evenings in Hegeman. Iron Man spent hours diagramming plays that he was certain could crush N.Y.U., and Muggsy agonized the dormitory by practicing on his clarinet—as though anybody cared how well the band played in the Yankee Stadium. Jeremy joined the ranks of happy rumor mongers. He talked of secret practices and of special plays that Rocky had been holding back for just this game. He talked of a substitute back who had been trained into a left-handed passer and of a new triple reverse that opened into a forward pass play with three or four lateral passes on the end of it. But all the time, while the excitement was boiling up inside him like a kettle left too long over a flame, Jeremy was talking through his hat and knew it. Muggsy and he planned on catching the 12:15 to New York on Saturday morning and after the game to meet Iron Man and go to a burlesque show.

On Friday night a rally for the team was held on Neilson Field. Muggsy brought his clarinet and Visch appeared with a cow bell. Jeremy trotted across the campus behind them with his heart thumping with the stored-up giddiness of a week of conjecture, hope, despair, and yearning. This rally would be special; Jeremy could feel the suspense building up, until he knew it had to break out somewhere unless they wanted the whole college to explode. This rally wasn't going to be a fiasco like the one before the Lafayette game when President Thomas had made a speech about owning a cane he refused to carry until Rutgers ended its six-year losing streak against Lafayette, and then some enterprising racketeer from the Beta house had stepped forth with an arm full of canes that he swore were exact replicas of the president's walking stick and everybody had been hoodwinked into paying a dollar for a cane that wasn't worth more than fifty cents. In the cold light of another Lafayette defeat the following afternoon the entire student body had been rather touchy about those canes; as Visch had said, President Thomas probably had taken a cut on every cane sold, and it was a cheap way for the president of a university to pick up his pin money. Even the rally before the Holy Cross game had been dull until after it was over, and the story was told of how the head cheerleader had swiped a petticoat from the clothesline behind the residence of the dean of men and soaking the garment in gasoline (siphoned from the dean's own car) had used it to ignite the bonfire. Taking the short cut through the dean's back yard, Jeremy chuckled at the discovery that tonight even the clothesline had been put away.

But the rally that evening was neither better nor worse than those that had preceded the Lafayette and Holy Cross games. The same speeches were made, the same cheers given, the same tunes thumped out by the college band; the bonfire crackled and roared, casting sinister shadows across the field and silhouetting the bare frames of the goal posts that on the morrow would be taken down for another year; and shivering uncomfortably as a cold, dry wind from across the Raritan curled around his legs and whispered that the first severe frost of the fall was only a few hours away, Jeremy could not shake off a feeling of disappointment. Visch muttered dispiritedly; two sophomores whom Jeremy did not know stirred restlessly; after the week of living for the N.Y.U. game the letdown was evident on every side. The dean of men sensed the danger in the moment; he spoke firmly.

"Men, you've had your fun. Now let's break it up quietly and get back to our respective living groups."

"Let's hang around until the old dean goes home to bed," Visch suggested.

"Then what?" The bite of the night air was awakening Jeremy to a pair of tired legs.

"There may be some fun."

Jeremy's crushed spirits began to lift; the sense of tight excitement crept back into his throat; he followed Visch down the path that circled the campus and would bring them ten minutes later back to the scene of the rally.

But when they completed circling the campus only half a dozen undergraduates lingered around the gates to Neilson Field. Jeremy felt certain their scheme had failed, but Visch shook his head. Then Muggsy appeared still carrying his clarinet.

"Go over to the Lambda Chi house and toot that thing a moment," Visch directed Muggsy.

Presently the stillness was broken by an explosion of notes from Muggsy's clarinet. A pause followed; four or five heads popped out of windows on the second floor; Muggsy obviously was explaining what was afoot. Again there came a pause; the windows closed; feet could be heard scrambling down the Lambda Chi porch.

"It's going to work!" Visch said as the group moved away from the shadows of the Neilson Field gate.

By the time they had rounded up the Chi Phis, the Chi Psis, and the Dekes there were more than a hundred undergraduates in the procession. And now the news that a victory parade was forming seemed to sprout its own wings to carry the word down the side thoroughfares and into Union Street where six fraternity houses were situated. Ford and Winants were emptied before the crowd passed either dormitory, and stragglers came running down College Avenue pulling on topcoats over their pajamas. Visch's eyes seemed a bit wild as he glanced back and calculated that there were between four and five hundred marchers behind him.

"The dean'll bust us both out of college if he finds out we're behind this," Jeremy said with a momentary constriction of conscience.

"He can't prove anything!"

"Where are we going now?"

"Across town to the College for Women!"

"How about the cops?"

Visch laughed. "When those hyenas see this mob they'll run for cover!"

When they reached George Street, there was no sign of the local constabulary anywhere; the street stretched ahead of them, quiet and deserted except for the evening trash piles before the silent stores. On the campus the parade had been fairly well organized, but here in the town the spirit of the mob began to exert itself. Within a block trash piles went sprawling into the street. A rolling milk bottle crashed against the curb. Singing, shouting, cheering, the crowd pushed on, its mischievious mood growing. At the corner of Paterson Street a dented Ford, toiling up the hill from the river, tried to edge its way through the paraders. When Jeremy saw the car again it was leading the procession with students covering all but a small space of the windshield through which the frightened face of the colored driver peered fretfully. A red-headed boy with a NO PARKING sign slung over his shoulder swung in between Visch and Jeremy; he offered to fight them both if they thought Rutgers was going to lose to N.Y.U. Muggsy pushed his way through the jostling throng, wailing that somebody had wrung his clarinet from his hands. But Visch spied the instrument in another moment; it had been passed up to a junior in pink pajamas who sat on the roof of the commandeered Ford. The boy could play it, too—lots better than Muggsy.

The clatter of upended ash cans subsided; the paraders had passed the main business section and were approaching the hill leading to the College for Women. The red-headed boy had abandoned the NO PARKING sign and carried one that said VEHICLES NOT PERMITTED ON THIS STREET; he waved the sign and with his mind on their destination lustily sang a ballad that described the misadventures of "Queen Aphrodite in her scant Egyptain nightie." The song had limitless possibilities, and the red-headed boy explored them all with a vehemence that soon reduced his bellows to a hoarse, croaking rasp. Visch glanced across at Jeremy and there was a faint gleam of worry in the junior's eyes; this mob was out of hand and nobody could predict what might happen with four or five hundred hoodlums running wild across the campus of the College for Women at ten minutes past midnight.

But when the paraders reached Nichol Avenue and the semicircle of two-story frame dwellings where many of the women students lived, an uncomfortable feeling of defeat settled down upon the crowd. There wasn't a light anywhere —not a solitary sign of life.

"Give 'em a cheer for that Big Red Team," someone suggested hopefully.

A voice shrieked, "Yee—eee—ow!"

But for the most part the cheer was given half-heartedly. Again there was a pause, then a light went on in one of the dormitory windows, a second light, a third. At the end of five minutes there was an audience of nine girls hanging over the window sills. The paraders tried to explain the reason for their merrymaking, but the girls weren't much interested.

"What's the sense of it?" one of them asked. "You're going to lose, anyway."

She was hooted down derisively.

The red-headed boy, still hoarse from his ballad to Aphrodite, mixed his metaphor eloquently. "Nothing but cows in this hen coop. Anybody can have the lot of 'em for one thin dime!"

"Sold!" shrieked the junior in pink pajamas who remained atop the commandeered Ford with Muggsy's clarinet under his arm.

In the tumult the lights in the dormitories went out and the windows slammed shut. But nobody cared. It was almost one, the edge was wearing off the escapade, and the increasing coldness of the early morning served to accentuate the weariness of the long trudge homeward. Then two Chi Phis in a roadster drove down the sidewalk, scattering the paraders. At the corner the car stopped while the driver reached out and pulled the handle on the fire box. In another moment off in the distance the fire siren wailed.

"Some fool always goes too far," Visch said angrily. "Come on, Muggsy, grab your clarinet. We're getting out of here now!"

By the time the trio from House Four reached George Street, they could hear a hook and ladder rolling down one of the side streets. They pressed on doggedly, not saying much, glad they had escaped. But once they reached the campus some of their bravado returned. It'd been an evening. It was the kind of story that could stand embellishment. It would tell well.

As they said good night on the doorstep of Hegeman Jeremy broke into a chuckle. "Think of those poor devils who play football," he said. "They had to be in bed by ten o'clock!"

IV

The morning started badly. Muggsy, sniffling with a cold, prowled around in his pajamas, so miserable and dejected that he didn't even worry over his turned-out navel. Iron Man, peeved to think that training rules had forced him to miss the fun, tried to torment Visch and Jeremy with the report that the old dean was wise to who the ringleaders had been and they could both expect to be expelled before nightfall.

"You should have seen those gals last night," Visch said. "One of them came out on the porch in her nightie and did a hula hula dance for us."

"Nuts," Iron Man said. His manner, however, was tinged with envious half-belief.

"It's the truth," Jeremy lied earnestly. "Ask Muggsy."

Muggsy sat on the stairway and moaned.

Classes were cut as a matter of principle. By eleven those students who were driving by car had departed, usually with horns honking as they drove by those buildings where a few desultory classes were still in session. Jeremy, Muggsy, and Visch were part of the throng that packed the New Brunswick railroad station by noon. Once the train pulled in everybody simply shoved; Jeremy, carried along by the crowd, dropped into a seat before he realized the other occupant was Earl Reed Silvers.

"Quite a night," Jeremy said.

"I've heard about it. Who started it?"

Jeremy hesitated. "Off the record?"

"Off the record."

Jeremy told him.

Professor Silvers smiled. For a moment he wondered how many such confidences he had shared during a lifetime on the campus. Sometime, in the years ahead, he thought that he might like to be dean of men. Somehow giving his life to boys was the only career he ever had wanted. He had written short stories and books for boys—over a thousand of one, twenty-seven of the other—and he had stuck at the job even though his friends had told him he was wasting his time. There was no big money in juveniles, and very little fame. But a boy wrote in with a problem and you tried to set him on the right track. That was one kind of reward. That boy who wrote you might have had eyes like Terrill's, or a smile that caught just a trifle at the corners. . . .

The train was passing through Metuchen. Professor Silvers leaned back against his seat and thought: Keep a boy honest and you needn't worry about the man. His glance shifted back to Jeremy.

"I read your story in the *Record* about Rocky," he said.

Jeremy had all but forgotten his midweekly sports story.

"Do you know Rocky, Jeremy?"

"No."

"Did you think that you might hurt a good guy—unfairly, unnecessarily?"

Jeremy shifted in his seat, feeling the warmth come into his face.

"I believe I'd think twice before I did a thing like that again, Jeremy," Professor Silvers said quietly.

"Yes, sir," the boy answered. He had never felt himself so thoroughly revealed as a cheat.

The sense of cheapness clung with him; even after they reached New York he couldn't shake off his dissatisfaction with himself. It spoiled the day. And the day was none too cheerful, anyhow. The skies above the Yankee Stadium were leaden and bleak. As Iron Man had predicted, as long as the Rutgers guards held up the game seemed like a contest, but midway through the second period the guards weakened. N.Y.U. won easily, 33 to 0. Iron Man held out for the burlesque show, but Jeremy shook his head. Those things were fakes—nothing but washed-out dames with screechy voices.

Riding home on the train, Jeremy wondered how Rocky felt over the defeat.

"Two good guards and we'd have taken 'em," Iron Man said.

"Too bad for Rocky we didn't take 'em," Visch said. "All the dissatisfied rah-rah boys will be after his scalp now."

Jeremy thought gloomily that no one had betrayed Rocky more than he. He hadn't been honest either with Rocky or himself.

"Wait until next year," Iron Man said.

"Every year it's the same old slop," Visch said. "Next year we'll probably lose by sixty points!"

Muggsy, almost asleep, rolled over and cushioned his head against the back of the seat. "Anyway," he announced, "our band played better than theirs!"

3

"GLADLY WOULD WE LEARN"

I

Iron Man's rebellion had been growing for a week. A cocoon-like emergence from athlete into scholar was a painful transformation that Iron Man suffered periodically—between football and wrestling in winter, and between wrestling and lacrosse in early spring. When these spells occurred Iron Man was a solemn, easily irritated individual who seemed to discover with a shock that classes and books were more than incidental sidelights to the ivy years; moreover Iron Man discovered that there existed on the faculty certain types of over-imaginative instructors who, at the scent of an athlete, appeared to react like hound dogs on a hunt. Iron Man had catalogued all of the characteristics by which he identified the species: a restless, waggish manner on the lecture platform; a nervous, roving eye that sought for the quarry; and then a persistent, heartless closing in for the kill. Under Marquess of Queensbury rules Iron Man thought that nobody should have to contend with more than one such adversary in any semester, but Iron Man found himself confronted with two—Dalmas in English and George in political science.

As Iron Man viewed his plight, he was becoming the victim of a squeeze play, for his Monday-Wednesday-Friday class schedule gave him a nine o'clock with George and a ten o'clock with Dalmas. He suspected collusion between his tormentors, for George invariably lectured five or ten minutes over the hour, heedless of the fact that Iron Man must travel three long blocks to his ten o'clock in Van Nest; and when Iron Man, breathless, determined, and hopelessly tardy, would burst into his English class, Dalmas would pause in his lecture, fix a cold, unforgiving glance upon the intruder, and say with the soft slash of razor-edged sarcasm, "Gentlemen, we will wait while Mr. Bartino makes his goal line stand!" Iron Man would slink off in humiliation to his seat, wanting nothing so much as a chance to engage Dalmas in a slugfest but thinking the better of the impulse, for Dalmas stood six-feet-four in his stocking feet and on a lecture platform looked nearer ten.

Jeremy and Muggsy could think the dilemma he faced very funny, but Iron Man didn't. On quiet autumn evenings coming back from Neilson Field he had often reflected on what being in college represented to him. He had dreamed of college since he had been a kid in short pants; but as much as anything college to Iron Man meant headlines in the Sunday sports sections. Guys like Visch said you were a fool to suffer the beating you received, the long hours, the wearisome practice, the self-abnegation that went with training, but those guys didn't understand. They thought it was only glory you were after, the roar of the crowd, the varsity letter on your sweater. Glory was fine, and the booming explosion of cheering thousands, and the youngsters who tagged along behind you with unblushing hero worship after a good game. But there was something more. You knew it playing on a rainy day when you crouched as the signals were called; your hands dug deep in the dirt, you could feel the mud oozing through your fingers, and somehow the strength of the soil to give energy to all living things became your strength, too. You knew it in a game when some opposing lineman played dirty in the pile-up and smashed his fist in your mouth or pounded his elbow into your groin, and on the next play you went for him and they carried him off the field looking like something that had come out of a meat grinder. You knew it at night when there were so many aches in your bones you gave up trying to tell them apart, but simply accepted yourself as one big ache, and then you went to bed and were blissfully asleep almost before you could snuggle the blanket around your shoulders.

Iron Man reckoned that he wasn't a fool giving his time to athletics. He knew himself. He was happy playing body contact games, pitting his strength against the best the opposition could throw at him, playing hard and tough and, if the other guy asked for it, playing nasty, too. He wanted to go on playing that way, and he respected the college for insisting on high scholastic standards for eligibility. Iron Man liked his college because it was tough about scholarship; he wasn't any dummy; he could buckle down and pass his work. A dogged schedule for studying was all you needed—his old high school coach had taught him that.

Iron Man played all games fair, including studying. But George and Dalmas had caught him off guard, and he was worried. If he fubbed those two courses he was in trouble scholastically; he'd get it bad from the coach, and worse from his old man when he went home. Nuts to that, said Iron Man's common sense with the eloquence of colloquial incisiveness. Iron Man had never run away from any adversary because of his size. He tackled Dalmas first. He wasn't asking Dalmas to give him special privileges, but, after all, could he help it if George neglected to dismiss the class on time?

"In this life, Mr. Bartino," Dalmas said, fumbling to keep the place in his book with his thumb, "you will find that no one much cares why you fail to fulfill your obligations. You either do or you don't."

"I'm only asking you to be reasonable about it, sir."

"Mr. Bartino, I find it difficult to be reasonable with football players. Football players think the college owes them an education and I don't!"

Iron Man's black eyes flashed. "If—if you knew anything about football players—or about football—"

Leaning against the side of the door, Dalmas seemed to tower above Iron Man like an angry eagle. "Listen, brother," he said in a decidedly unprofessorial tone, "when I was out for football I could have taken a dozen guards like you and dumped them on their fannies!"

Iron Man doubted it; he most certainly doubted it. If Mr. Dalmas would like to put on a uniform and come out onto Neilson Field and try—

"Mr. Bartino," Mr. Dalmas said, coldly, "I should like to quote a passage from Shakespeare to you: 'Men have died from time to time, and worms have eaten them, but not for love.'"

Iron Man stomped away, flustered and raging, and it did not improve his disposition on opening a magazine that evening to discover that the featured story was a college football story and its author was Herbert Dalmas. Muggsy scarcely improved the situation with another of his inevitable limericks:

> There once was a Prof named Herb
> Who thought football players absurd
> He needled their pride
> Shot darts in their hide
> And gave them—ahem—the bird!

Iron Man stalked away, disgusted. If Dalmas wouldn't give him a break, his last hope was George. On Wednesday morning when Iron Man joined Jeremy to go over to George's nine o'clock in political science Iron Man was chuckling. In one hand he carried a notebook, in the other an alarm clock.

Jeremy pointed to the clock. "What's that for?"

"You'll see!"

Jeremy couldn't concentrate on George's lecture for thinking of the clock ticking steadily on toward the hour of ten. At five minutes to the hour he stole a glance toward Iron Man, but Iron Man hardly fluttered a lash, and listened with dispassionate detachment as the instant of his retribution drew near. Professor George, an incurable punster, was embarked on a lecture about the highest judicial tribunal in the Nation—"the Shoe Cream Court." He was talking of a justice from Ohio—but he said "Oh-ho." Jeremy looked at his watch. It was seconds before ten, but George was rushing on as though the hour had hardly begun.

The alarm went off with a fearful clatter. George stopped in the middle of a word, his head coming up with a jerk and seeming to hang in mid-air as though thrust there on the end of a pike. The mixture of emotion revealed in George's face was wonderful to recognize: shock, bewilderment, slow comprehension, the first faintly pinkish tinge of indignation. The class had collected its wits; the clang of the alarm was lost momentarily in deep-bellied, explosive laughter. Jeremy watched Iron Man, and Iron Man simply sidled over to the window, hoisted himself upon the sill, and dropped out of sight. He wasn't going back to claim his clock. He gave it forthwith, anonymously and with a full heart, to the Department of History and Political Science.

II

For a week Iron Man glowed with the flush of his victory over Professor George. But stormier days were ahead for Iron Man—days when the intellectual aspects of his existence were to set him at war within himself, although he no longer stood alone against the battlements of learning. When the bombshell of Darwinism burst upon Hegeman, there were few among its inhabitants unscarred by the searing fragments.

The change came with unexpected suddenness; one evening the occupants of Hegeman were content to discuss football prospects and the outrageous prices in the college book store, and the next the bomb had been exploded beneath their intellectual complacency. The cause of the upheaval was a freshman course in history intended to survey in two short semesters the entirety of man's recorded story from the cave through the industrial revolution with side excursions into anthropology, economics, comparative religion, sociology, psychology, political science, and philosophy. This course, listed modestly in the college catalogue under the title of contemporary civilization, held an irresistible appeal to most freshmen; they felt that to have their heads crammed so full of scraps of knowledge of every shape and variety for only eight dollars a semester hour (no more than they were charged for college algebra and English composition) was getting their hands on a bargain. Jeremy was delighted with the course since he liked to carry home some proof that the family bank account was not being depleted without good cause, and to him contemporary civilization became the gateway to what seemed to be an all-inclusive erudition. Mom and pop were happy because Jeremy was happy explaining that *pithecanthropus erectus* was the technical term by which one designated the first cave man capable of toddling around on two limbs instead of four, or that the Nebular Hypothesis made perfectly clear from where the universe had come (but not, unfortunately, whither it was going). In such moments Jeremy appeared to become the embodiment of one of those full-page advertisements for the *Book of Knowledge* or for Dr. Eliot's five-foot shelf, a highly satisfying sensation.

Jeremy's section of the course was taught by Edward McNall Burns, who, from one point of view, could almost have been accused of looking down upon the thirty eager, awestruck faces turned toward him each Tuesday, Thursday, and Saturday with something of the dispassion with which a scientist would look down upon thirty guinea pigs. In a sense Jeremy and his classmates were guinea pigs; as Burns lectured his mind was storing away that amazing assortment of facts that freshmen on college campuses everywhere now encounter between the covers of his stupendous textbook, *Western Civilizations.* Had Jeremy and his cronies had the least inkling of this fact, they very likely would have demanded a cut on the royalties, but not knowing they placed Burns upon a pedestal; to see this straight, dark-browed figure on the lecture platform, coat buttoned, tie set just right, hair meticulously parted in the middle, was to behold the oracle; for fifty minutes he would lecture without stopping, skipping from Greek to Roman culture with the poise of enormous erudition, revealing a prodigious memory that seemed outright bottomless, and all the while Jeremy would scribble down notes and hope frantically that he could remember just one small fraction of the wisdom that Burns so obviously and so patently possessed.

It never seemed to occur to Jeremy in his breathless admiration that Burns had devoted his lifetime to mastering his subject; it never seemed to impress him that there were other men in the department who taught the subject with the same adeptness, or that even Burns probably had to refresh his memory from notes before each class. Jeremy was simply overwhelmed and hung onto the ropes of learning as Muggsy's clarinet hung onto a sour note—a bit desperate in his perseverance. As the first few weeks of the fall sped by, Jeremy sat with mouth agape as Burns led him from the cave to the splendid age of Pericles, and thence by rather quick hops to Darwinism. Burns devoted three lecture hours to the theory of evolution, but the lodgers in House Four were in no mood to deal so summarily with Darwin.

Iron Man, emerging from the showers with the hairiest chest Jeremy ever had seen, stood with a towel draped over his knees, and unburdened his troubled heart. "I'm no monkey descendant, see? I've got beliefs. I've never missed mass once in ten years. Don't tell me all religion is nonsense!"

The Haldeman-Julius sage spoke jeeringly. "You can't prove there's a God!"

"Who says I can't?"

"I do! I'd like to see you prove it."

"What do you want? Photographs?"

"Or somebody who's seen God getting waited on in Macy's bargain basement?" Muggsy asked.

The Haldeman-Julius sage laughed. He was a thin-boned boy sorely troubled with pimples, and Jeremy reflected cynically that doubtless that was as good a reason as any for embracing atheism. The little blue book collector pressed on doggedly. "Prove there's a God. Go on and prove it!"

"Go prove nuts!" Iron Man said.

"What's that got to do with God?"

"Nothing. And neither has a poke in the teeth but you're going to get one in two seconds."

"So God is brute force? Then Napoleon was God—and Charlemagne and Genghis Khan?"

"Shut up!"

"Or maybe God was the cave man with the biggest club, or—"

Iron Man started down the hall with a menacing gleam in his eyes, but the Haldeman-Julius sage was an agile young rascal. He bounced into his room, slammed the door, and hooted derisively as the lock snapped.

Visch tried to sound conciliatory. "Look here, Iron Man, have you ever read Darwin's *Descent of Man* or his *Origin of the Species?*"

"No, and I don't intend to!"

Visch demanded quietly, "But what's so wrong with what Darwin said? He believed principally that life started with one cell and that environment shaped and reshaped the form of various animals as life cells welded together into more complex organisms. How do you think you were created—in your mother's womb?"

Iron Man looked embarrassed and Visch snorted angrily.

"You dumb cluck! In case you'd like to know you began as a single cell. One puny cell that split into two parts and then into four. Don't look so goofy. What did you think happened—that you sprang full born like Minerva from the ear of Zeus?"

Iron Man didn't say what he thought. He was confused. With what little of his dignity remained, he squared his shoulders and stalked off to his own room.

Jeremy was almost as troubled as Iron Man. Religion seemed such a personal affair that a man should be left alone to believe what he wanted to believe. But doubts had been stirred up in Jeremy's mind, and they lay there to plague him in unexpected moments. Halfway through donning his pajamas he thudded down the stairs in his bare feet to Muggsy's room.

"Do you believe in prayer, Muggsy?"

"Sure. Don't you?"

Jeremy nodded. Prayer had been a habit trained into him since childhood. He accepted prayer as natural and had believed that everyone he knew prayed at night just as they brushed their teeth.

"What do you pray for, Muggsy?"

"Oh, just things that are on my mind."

"Things that you want?"

"Sure. And for my mother and dad. And that we'd beat N.Y.U."

"I guess you didn't pray hard enough for that one, Muggsy."

"I never thought it would do much good, but it seemed worth a try."

Muggsy began sorting out the medicine bottles on his dresser. He took a swig of a vile-appearing concoction, then a gulp of mineral oil. He sprayed his throat and used some nose drops. There was a great capacity for blind faith in Muggsy. When Jeremy left the room Muggsy was laboriously salving his chest with Vicks.

In bed, watching the lights gleaming through the windows of the theological seminary dormitory over on Holy Hill, Jeremy continued to think about prayer. If a man prayed and felt elevated in spirit, if he reached out his hand toward God and experienced a comforting union of child with parent, if he humbled himself willingly and reverently and felt purged by the acceptance of another force—a greater force—beyond his own flesh and bone, what else need he explain? The experience was complete, the man believed, and his spirit found sources of radiance as it did at the sight of an all-gold sky at twilight, or in the touch of the wind against his skin on a spring day, or in the heavy whiteness of the hemlock branches after a snowfall. Not everything in life could be explained unless the simple beauty of truth itself were to lose its indestructibility. Coleridge had the best answer—religion begins and ends in the heart. Jeremy rolled over and closed his eyes; mysticism was a soothing cloak to draw over the spare bones of imagination.

Not many evenings later Jeremy came into House Four to find Muggsy reading the Bible.

"I read it from cover to cover once a year," Muggsy said.

Jeremy had never read the Bible. He began that night. Once as he turned a page a thought pleased him. Did Edward McNall Burns ever suspect where his lectures on Darwinism had led them?

III

In retrospect Jeremy agreed with Thoreau that in the memorable moments of life men are more inclined to remember how they itched, not how their hearts beat. And on looking back the assortment of rooms where he sat hour after

hour taking notes, listening, day-dreaming, napping, whispering, laughing, squirming, groaning, learning and forget-
ting never failed to astonish him: history in an old, remod-
eled mansion with parquet floors, high and dusty ceilings,
marble fireplaces and filigreed moldings; German in the tur-
ret of New Jersey Hall, the most insane example of architec-
ture on the campus, where the builder, never stumped for a
novel embellishment, had placed a false window in one of
the chimneys; economics in a dumpy little residence where
on a spring morning the sickish odor of sulphur drifted over
from the Chemistry Building; English on the top floor of
Van Nest, a structure as square and unimaginative as a soap
box, with two flights of stairs to climb and then, where a coal
stove had stood in the old days, a plugged-up pipe opening to
gaze upon for an hour, three days a week; algebra and trig-
onometry and Spanish in beautiful Old Queen's where some
of the initials on the bubble glass in the windows had been
scratched a century before; philosophy on a warm day out
under the trees of the campus because the instructor had
been as badly affected as Jeremy by spring fever; and geology
in a tall, rectangular building where in the last row Jeremy's
vision appeared to be distorted so that the lecturer's head
seemed to end on top like a Brazil nut.

Jeremy possessed strong opinions concerning the men who
were his teachers, and quoted with relish Henry Adams's observation that "no man, however strong, can serve ten years
as schoolmaster, priest or senator, and remain fit for anything
else." Even as a freshman Jeremy could understand that in
all three of these professions—and in teaching particularly—
there existed a certain implied subservience on the part of
pupil to master that produced a sense of artificial importance. The professors who instructed him were human and
did well to hold onto that conviction at any cost; they knew
a great deal but also had forgotten not a little that they could
not recall without a hasty retreat to their sources, and so a

certain humility before God and their fellow men was not altogether unbecoming; and while they were extremely well informed in their special fields and deserved respect for their intellectual accomplishment, still their judgments were not infallible on all things. If the ivy years were to teach Jeremy anything, the first lesson observed, as he sat in detached judgment of the men who taught him, was simply the fact that dogmatism was no more beneficial to a learned man than to an ignorant one, stubbornness no less revealing of frustration, cynicism no less indicative of inward defeat.

It was certainly more comfortable for Jeremy to blame his instructor rather than himself for his shortcomings in a course; aside from football, this indulgence became his favorite sport. The appearance of a new member on the faculty set the campus grapevine buzzing. Was he tough on athletes? A good lecturer? A rat who sprung surprise quizzes on the Saturday of a big week end? A fair marker? Susceptible to leg pulling? Irascible at class cutting? By the answers to these questions Jeremy decided whose classes were to be avoided at any cost. But Jeremy was loyal to his favorites; he was among that ardent coterie who championed Billy Twiss as one of the princes of the teaching profession, a man whose shyness almost reached diffidence, and so obscured in large measure his greatness.

On the campus Twissy seemed just another middle-aged recluse who carried a brown brief case and hid behind a cigar; but in the classroom he became at once a warm, rich personality, a man of deep gentleness of manner, of abundant kindliness, of keen intellect and a never failing sense of humor. There wasn't a particle of conceit or affectation in Twissy; he detested sham and tinsel, and his New England conscience, bred in the marrow of his bones, had ripened into an intellectual forthrightness that set him apart as an instinctive scholar and gentleman. He was hesitant in his speech and had a habit of leaving off in the middle of a sentence while his mind groped for the precise words to give full body to his thought. One day there was a long pause as Twissy, eyes closed, searched through the corridors of his mind for those words that would fix forever the point he wished to make. The silence became painfully prolonged, and then a wit in the class said, "I do believe he's dead!" The room erupted into explosive merriment, but Twissy was master of the moment.

"You may go now, gentlemen," he announced, "but please go quietly for there are other classes sleeping in this building."

Twissy's style as a teacher was never theatrical nor spectacular, and he never rated too high in those annual polls conducted by the undergraduate newspaper to determine the most popular professor on the campus. And yet there was something about Twissy that in time grew on Jeremy, a deep earnestness perhaps, an eagerness to give something real, something that Jeremy could hang onto forever. In freshman year Twissy taught composition, in sophomore year American literature, in junior year literary criticism, in senior year advanced American lit. He taught with all his heart, and yet with a scholar's pride, refusing to debase his love for fine writing by reducing it to silly formulas that might become meaningless, if fanciful, catchwords in an uncomprehending mind. What he endeavored to do was one of those bold, courageous feats too little encountered these days in the teaching of English. But Twissy understood that before literature can have genuine meaning there must come first an appreciation of language. He understood as well a serious and crippling burden that in recent years had been thrust upon the teachers of English in American colleges—that the substitution of modern languages for the classics had failed to give students that natural flair of expression in English which in the old days came from a mastery of Greek and Latin. In his own manner Twissy tried to compensate for this betrayal by instilling in the hearts of his students a love for words—words used precisely, with zest and style. He taught grammar in the same spirit—commas and hyphens and semicolons as something alive, something that gave balance and emphasis and vigor to words as they wound around a thought and made it captive. He taught composition according to the time-honored form of an introduction, a middle and a conclusion, but he tried to breathe a soul into the so often sterile body, crying *"You!"* Writing, Twissy taught, was not a mechanical chore, like the solution of a rudimentary algebraic equation, but an experience in which feeling motivated thought, and the faith of the heart supported the reflection of the mind. So great a lesson could not be taught easily or quickly.

Many of Jeremy's classmates passed by Twissy when they could have studied under him. If Twissy had been a trickster on the lecture platform he might have attracted some; if he had been less honest, admitting not so freely his own weaknesses or discovering where his students were guilty of mental slovenliness and imitation, he might have been more popular; or if he had reconciled himself to the norm, rather than to setting the true scholar's value on effort and integrity, he might have gained a reputation as a more lenient marker. But Twissy, in a sense, was a patient plodder; he was willing always to wait, to watch, and to hope.

Jeremy's hero among the men who taught him was Twissy but Muggsy's hero was Dickie Morris—Dickie who had been teaching mathematics for so long that Muggsy swore George III had sent him along with the charter for the college in 1766. A thin, rather smallish man with obviously a wiry strain, Dickie could outwalk Muggsy and nine out of ten other undergraduates, for in everything he said and did a boyish exuberance revealed how alert his mind had grown with the years, how warm his heart. For Visch, who had been bullied into taking Greek by the dean, William Hamilton Kirk was the greatest scholar on the campus. A man well along in the twilight years, tall, thin, stoop-shouldered, no one had ever seen Dr. Kirk without a pile of books in his arms; he was, as Visch could attest, a strict disciplinarian who had no patience with the unprepared student, but no mind ever played so nimbly with the wisdom of the centuries or fitted more naturally those lines by Shakespeare—

> *He was a scholar, and a ripe and good one;*
> *Exceeding wise, fair-spoken, and persuading;*
> *Lofty and sour to them that loved him not,*
> *But to those that sought him sweet as summer.*

Jeremy could take pride in the fact that he recognized Twissy's greatness despite the barriers of diffidence and hesitancy that Twissy seemed to erect around himself, yet in his heart Jeremy knew that he was giving in return only that meager amount of effort absolutely required to pass his course in freshman English. His conscience should have troubled him more at this admission that all of Twissy's kindliness and gentleness were being so poorly repaid; indeed, there came moments when he resolved to do better, but those moments were short-lived; it was not a matter of wavering in his affection toward Twissy, but merely a necessity borne of being driven in other courses that taxed his native abilities more strenuously than freshman English. Burns's course in contemporary civilization was all memory, a prodigious chore that Jeremy resented when he considered how much of his leisure time it consumed. Geology he slighted as much as he dared; he had to take one science and so had selected geology because he believed it easier than physics or chemistry. But he had no real interest in earth formations or the names of rocks; the field trips to the Perth Amboy clay pits in search of the remnants of dinosaur footprints annoyed him, because by the time the class returned by bus to the campus an entire afternoon had been lost; and the lab sessions in paleontology, taking two hours out of the heart of another afternoon each week, bored him because he had no interest whatever in the remains of dead fish. The department's paleontologist was a short, neatly groomed, fair-skinned Icelander named Helgi Johnson; and the most impressive fact Jeremy retained from his entire year in geology was the surprising information that for one night Helgi Johnson had played saxophone with Guy Lombardo's orchestra.

By fair luck or foul Jeremy was passing in English, contemporary civilization and geology, and while his contentment in this knowledge may not have been complete at least it was sufficient to permit him to live comfortably with his conscience. German and algebra were other matters. Jeremy selected German for his foreign language because he had been fed up with Spanish in high school. He had no better excuse, and so he jumped from an Iberian frying pan into a Teutonic fire. His lips and throat were entirely maladjusted to German gutteralism; nothing about the language fitted his temperament. And his instructor was a mild-mannered, simple-hearted man lacking the backbone to insist that he master the subject; in truth, the man seemed entirely blind to the fact that practically everyone cribbed on tests. Rather than flunk the course, and so have a black mark against his record, Jeremy pleaded with his instructor to allow him to drop the subject. The instructor agreed.

"He gave you a break," Muggsy said.

But Jeremy merely shrugged. He had known no respect in high school for teachers who had been bullied by their students; he saw no reason for respecting them in college.

He ran up against a tartar in algebra, however. This course was taught by a fiery-tempered German Jew who quite obviously regretted the passing of the birch cane from the American schoolroom. If anyone failed his course he considered that performance a personal affront, and when his emotions exploded there was a good chance that the blackboard eraser would go sailing across the room.

Jeremy's weakness in algebra was spotted almost at once, and the instructor descended with a roar.

"Damn you, Baxter, you get this stuff in your head!"

"I'm trying, sir!"

" 'I'm trying, sir! I'm trying, sir!' " The instructor, mimicking Jeremy, reduced his tone to a nasal whine. "You damn well better try, Baxter! See me in my office this afternoon at four o'clock."

Jeremy climbed the two flights of stairs to the instructor's office not knowing quite what to expect. But the man greeted him civilly. For the next two hours Jeremy was tutored privately—and without charge—in algebra. The instructor's driving determination to have every student master the subject matter in his course was overpowering; after five such sessions Jeremy passed algebra, and he was grateful for that fact even though he achieved the goal by sheer force of rote learning without ever once feeling the joy of letting his mind escape into the free air of presuppositions, which is the essence of mathematics; and yet when he tried to thank his instructor for the many hours of tutoring gratuitously given, the man lost all of his bluster and blushed like a schoolgirl. When at the end of the year his mathematics teacher was dropped from the faculty, Jeremy believed that the college administration had made the mistake of confusing the fellow's bark with his bite; on the other hand, the news that the instructor who had permitted him to drop German had also been let go neither surprised nor disturbed him.

So, day by day, more unconsciously than consciously, Jeremy grew to know the faculty under whom he had come to study. There had never been, and he sensed there could never be, any guaranteed common denominator among the members of the faculty as personalities. Some were drivers and others were shirkers, some were tactful and gentle and others were blunt and explosive, some were punsters and others were more humorless than tapioca pudding, some were colored in judgment by their prejudices and their vanities and others were colorless no matter from what perspective they were viewed, some like Burns were astonishingly erudite and others like Twissy, Kirk and Dickie Morris were capable of arousing happy affections. The test of a faculty was not any one individual but its collective effect; could it bring to life a line in Chaucer—

Gladly would we learn, and gladly teach.

IV

As teachers, the Twissys, the Dickies, the Kirks could ascribe their greatness not so much to the subject matter of their courses as to a certain imitative instinct that they could inspire. It was no small accomplishment that a Muggsy who only half a dozen years ago had wanted to be a second Babe Ruth now understood that to become a second Dickie Morris would be as good, if not better. And if Visch remarked one night in satirizing William Hamilton Kirk, "I am like a book in breeches!" (not knowing that he quoted Sydney Smith's quip about Macaulay), it was still the attitude that mattered —an attitude that accepted college as an environment in which books became one of the natural concomitants of healthy existence.

Because this attitude existed, however, Jeremy and Iron Man became involved in a law suit and Muggsy slept through the most exciting night in one hundred and seventy years of Rutgers history. The trouble began about a month after college opened—on an evening in early October when a chill wind moaned through the hemlocks on Bishop Campus—and an old gentleman with crisp white hair, glasses on a long black ribbon, and a neatly trimmed Van Dyke beard came into Hegeman. There was a mark of distinction about the old fellow, the air of a scholar. He spoke in a rich voice with rather a heavy Harvard accent, and his natty attire combined with his convivial spirit gave the impression that here stood

a man who had locked arms with the world and had saun-
tered jauntily along the boulevards of experience. At a guess
Jeremy would have said that the visitor to House Four was a
professor or one of the deans or perhaps another college
president in search of Dr. Thomas's residence. In the case of
Mr. Kelly, appearances were not only deceiving but also
costly; Mr. Kelly's mission in life was the selling of books.

Mr. Kelly knew his business as expertly as Twissy knew
grammar or William Hamilton Kirk knew Greek; and as a
champion Mr. Kelly had no intention of dissipating his talent on small fry. For five dollars on signing a contract, and
then for the trifling matter of three dollars a month, Mr.
Kelly proposed to make of each resident of House Four the
proprietor of a handsome set of books. How many of the resi-
dents of the other houses of Hegeman were persuaded under
the spell of Mr. Kelly's jovial approbation for all patrons of
the arts to part with the better share of a week's food allowance Jeremy could not know; the fact remained that in another fortnight the expressman delivered to Jeremy's room
thirteen volumes of the plays of Hendrik Ibsen and that Iron
Man became the startled owner of a staggering number of
volumes of the collected works of Richard Harding Davis.
A freshman in House Three invested in the collected works
of Thomas Hardy, and there were rumors of a sophomore in
House Six who had thrown all reason to the winds, had
bought thirty volumes of Joseph Conrad, and was in hock for
nine months longer than either Jeremy or Iron Man.

Iron Man never read more than a dozen pages of Richard
Harding Davis during his four years at college, and at best
Jeremy read two of the Ibsen plays. But ominously, on the
first day of every month, along came the publisher's bill for
three dollars, and then after four or five months when Jeremy
or Iron Man neglected to send a check a series of weekly letters appeared in their mail boxes. At first these appeals for a
prompt remittance were models of courtesy and tact, but

midway through their sophomore year when their payments were eight or nine months delinquent (and when, to tell the whole grim story, the stamping on the backbones of the books had faded to a point where the titles were no longer distinguishable) the letters grew more belligerent. But by then Jeremy and Iron Man were beyond the ethics of the case; their indebtedness was more than a month's spending money and the publisher had no wish to see his books returned. And so it happened that in their senior year Jeremy and Iron Man were sued for the balance of their accounts, or rather as a preliminary to suit were summoned to appear before the publisher's legal representative. Eighteen undergraduates were in the same sad predicament, and were forced to wait in a stuffy little anteroom until the lawyer could see each individually. Few of the eighteen defendants had been close friends until this moment of jeopardy, but now they stood together, inseparable comrades, proud and defiant, the College versus the Outer World; and then into the anteroom popped a prelegal student who had heard of the trouble. Few recognized him; he was of that tribe of undergraduates who live far down the dark hallways of rooming houses, who eat by themselves in fly-specked restaurants downtown, and who are seldom seen except in class or deep in the bowels of the library bookstacks. Behind his heavy rimmed glasses flashed a pair of fiery, scholarly eyes; he fixed them on the crowd in the anteroom.

"Listen," he said in a thin, excited voice, "none of you was twenty-one when you signed those contracts. They're not legal. Don't let that squirt in there bully you with any threats of suit. If he gets nasty you just tell him—"

Jeremy and Iron Man told him. The lawyer threw up his hands. Today the prelegal student is one of his partners.

Throughout the freshman year a steady procession of book salesmen continued to march into House Four. As the early bird who had gathered the most worms, Mr. Kelly stood apart; those of his brethren who followed him into House Four were of plainly a seedier caste, and the quality of their merchandise even more questionable; for the most part they were peddling various items of erotica. Muggsy bit on the bait, and found that he had encumbered himself with some excessively dull reading; what was even more outrageous the volumes were barred from the mails and so had to be delivered by express at a time when Muggsy could not be in his room to receive them, necessitating a two-mile hike over and back from Hegeman to the express office at Raritan Station. Not many days before Twissy had remarked, twisting his foot against the floor and gazing sheepishly out the window, that considering all the exploitation made of it sex was the most overrated commodity in the world, and walking back from Raritan Station with two cheaply manufactured books under his arm to show for the effort Muggsy agreed with Twissy. Wearied by the trek Muggsy fell into a slumber so sound that he did not awaken until after ten the following morning. To have slept through three classes for an assortment of frowsy hoydens who hadn't breathed in two thousand years was in itself sound education, Muggsy suspected; but to have slept as well through the night when the old gymnasium burned to the ground and the remainder of the undergraduates in Hegeman had sported themselves dancing around in pajamas, impeding the heroic struggles of the local fire fighters, and succeeding in the end in making off with the fire chief's hat and one of his ladders was, to put it bluntly, too hard a price to pay for a concubine dead or alive. Muggsy never forgave himself.

The book salesman had his easiest pickings in the first few weeks of freshman year, but the competition soon stiffened— from the sale of football tickets, for one thing; and from the appearance of the magazine agency men, for another. As the ivy years passed Jeremy watched the mounting piles of technical and scientific journals subscribed to by freshmen eager to establish themselves in their chosen careers; the magazine salesmen well knew that human nature is at no time half so weak as in the first bloom of ambition to become a professional man, and so each earnest young engineer or chemist or botanist or agriculturist was signed to a five- or ten- or twenty-year subscription to the most advanced journal in his field before he had learned how to use a slide rule or to clean a Bunsen burner. But considered objectively, the periodic arrival on the campus of the book vendors and the magazine agents was more to be tolerated than deplored; they brought to Muggsy, Jeremy, and Iron Man an awareness of how intimately the ivy years were linked with the printed word; but, even so, once every six weeks when marking period tests rolled around, they appeared to rediscover this fact the painful way.

V

Jeremy could avoid the evil hour no longer. His first six-week tests began on the morrow—one at eight o'clock with Burns in contemporary civilization and another at ten with Twissy in English. Jeremy sat at his desk determined to cram into his head in the next seven or eight hours the neglected lessons of the past month and a half. As he faced the pile of books before him—three textbooks in C.C. and one ponderous volume on prose writing in English—he was aghast to realize how far behind he had fallen in his work. Rather sickly Jeremy was seeing clearly that the college community was so organized that if the will to study were left to the weakness of the flesh nobody ever studied. Even now when the moment of retribution loomed only a few scant hours away distractions abounded—the monotonous bounce of a tennis ball against the wall as Muggsy continued six months ahead of time to condition himself as a candidate for the frosh team, the loud strum of a mandolin as Visch awaited the time to go off to Perth Amboy to work on his model dental drills. Stoically Jeremy tried to shut these noises from his mind. He had to get this stuff into his head! But still the bounce of the tennis ball persisted, and, even more disturbing, the voice of Jeremy's conscience. College was not designed for the loafer and the bluffer. As Dalmas had told Iron Man, nobody cared why a student failed to fulfill his obligations—he either did or he didn't. The marks Jeremy made on those tests tomorrow were going into the books to stay. Essentially college was a serious business.

Visch went off to Perth Amboy and Muggsy tired of hitting the tennis ball. In the stillness that descended upon House Four, Jeremy began to read. But in his heart he knew that he didn't know how to study. Every sentence, every fact impressed him with its overwhelming importance, and he tried to pound them all into his memory. By the end of half an hour he had quit the chair by the desk and was curled up on the bed, gibbering to himself like a Mongoloid idiot as he attempted to fix in his mind what he already had read. He was tensed and unhappy. He was a fool for not having studied this stuff day by day as Muggsy had.

Jeremy groaned. He had to get this stuff and get it tonight. Back at the desk he began to read once more—doggedly, disgusted with himself, for he sensed that he could have enjoyed much of what he was reading removed from the desperation with which he now worked against time. He kept on, fighting against a sudden drowsiness, then discovering with dismay that he had been reading only words and would have to re-read the page for its meaning. But all the time the clock ticked on and the hollow restlessness within Jeremy expanded. In his agitation the boy could not comprehend all that was happening to him. Months hence he would understand—but not tonight. Slowly, painfully the comprehension would come that with the impulse to study there had to be an awareness of where study was leading. The correlation of one subject to another was the thing that gave a heart lift to the task of studentship. Then no part of scholarship stood alone, but was bound forever with the destiny of humanity. Then study transcended drudgery and become alive—an unending drama with exciting scenes and fascinating denouements. Then one day history could be a set of facts from a remote age preserved in a textbook, a month hence it could explain the background whence a literary style and form had evolved, a year hence it could be discovered to have left a political philosophy woven into the constitution of a nation, and ten or twenty or fifty years later it could set the stage for a debate on the floor of Congress or explain why men had shaped their houses according to certain models or reveal the causation behind a bitter dispute between capital and labor. Then every field of knowledge could begin to hold such clues; then through study any undergraduate could begin to grow into the one truly immortal Sherlock Holmes, for the crime he was seeking to solve for himself and for the world was man's recurring inhumanity to man. But tonight Jeremy was oblivious to these truths. One reason why was simply the fact that he had fallen asleep at his desk.

Visch, coming back from Perth Amboy, awakened him. It was quarter after eleven. Jeremy sat upright, dazed and alarmed.

"My gosh, Visch, I've got a hundred pages to wade through yet."

"It's no good, kid. You can't do it that way. You know more about this junk than you think. After all, these lectures you've been hearing more or less repeat what's in your books. Get your sleep and trust to the gods on what you know now."

"Visch," Jeremy wailed, "I'm going to flunk."

"Then flunk. You've got two more six-week periods in which to make it up."

Jeremy's conscience still bothered him; he should have another crack at those books. Visch shrugged and walked away, and Jeremy, looking after him, knew that he was licked. He tumbled into bed and slept fretfully.

In the morning he did badly on both tests, though as the day wore on and he could compare answers with Muggsy and Iron Man he began to gain confidence that he had just squeezed by with a grade of sixty. He remained shaken, however.

That night, the moment Jeremy returned to Hegeman from supper, he opened his books. Resolved to turn over a new leaf and to do each day's work as it came, he had been reading for twenty minutes when a commotion in the courtyard distracted his attention. He went to the window and looked down. Muggsy and Iron Man were creeping along the wall dragging an enormous pile of junk behind them.

"What's up?" Jeremy called down.

"Muggsy's been saving newspapers," Iron Man replied. "Must have half a ton of them. That slob who's always messing up the showers with his papers is out and his window's open."

Jeremy glanced back at his books, but only fleetingly. "Wait up. I'm coming down!"

Muggsy and he hoisted Iron Man through the window and then tossed in bundle after bundle of papers. Iron Man worked quickly and efficiently. He stuffed the bed with papers, the pillow cases, the desk, the closet, the radio. Then, standing on the window sill, he showered papers wherever they would fall.

Muggsy was elated. He danced around, chortling. Jeremy's own animal spirits soared.

"Say, Muggsy, why don't we go downtown for a soda?"

"It's getting late."

"Lots of places are open yet. Anyway, I know a couple of guys down in Winants who are swiping a red light to hang on the dean's porch."

"No kiddin'!" Muggsy danced around with another fit of chortling.

It was one in the morning when Jeremy returned to his room. The light on his desk still burned above the open book. But Jeremy didn't notice the book. He simply switched off the light and dropped down on the bed, exhausted.

4

THE TARGUM

I

The offices of the undergraduate newspaper, *The Targum,* were housed in a three-story frame building, repainted every two years the same hideous shade of canary yellow.

"So you edited your high school paper," said the sophomore news editor who interviewed Jeremy. "So you're the correspondent for your home town newspaper. Where would you like to begin on *The Targum*—writing the editorials?"

"I can write editorials," Jeremy admitted.

"Sorry. We have an editor-in-chief who writes editorials. But the news room needs a good sweeping. You'll find a broom in the hall closet!" The sophomore news editor walked away as though he could no longer bear to despoil himself with such foolish chatter.

Jeremy leaned against the hallway banister, sulking. Bewildered, hurt, he could see in the chambers beyond the exciting activity of which he had every expectation of becoming a part—undergraduate reporters, their hats tipped back, bent trance-like over their typewriters; a tall boy in a white sweater hung over the telephone in deep communion with someone at the College for Women; the sophomore news editor playing mumble-the-peg with a pair of scissors on the top of a battered, unpainted table. Jeremy advanced into the room, determined to have this thing out.

The sophomore news editor stopped him. "Floors all swept?"

"No, they're not swept!"

"Well, hurry up and sweep 'em!"

Jeremy stood in the momentary impotence of a mounting fury as the sophomore news editor balanced the points of the scissors on the edge of his shoulder for a throw that threatened to split the table or sever the ears of a toiling reporter in the immediate foreground.

"Somebody has to sweep the floors," the sophomore news editor said as he braced himself to flip the scissors. "The college insists on it. Cuts down on the janitor upkeep, you see."

"After I sweep the floors, then what?"

"We'll try you out on a news assignment."

"Like what?"

"Like seeing if any of the campus buildings are on fire while you empty the waste baskets in the incinerator behind the garage."

"And if none of them are on fire?"

"Then you won't have any story to write so you can run over to Nick the tailor and get the suit I left there this morning to be pressed."

The scissors flashed through the air and luckily struck the table top. Jeremy slammed his hat on his head. The light was on in Silvers's office as Jeremy walked down the path past Old Queen's. The boy couldn't resist sharing his outrage with the man.

But Silvers seemed to think that what the sophomore news editor had proposed was funny. "He's right, you know. Somebody does have to sweep the floors."

Jeremy remained stubborn. "I can get along without *The Targum*."

Silvers nodded. "*The Targum* can get along without you, too, but I had hoped you'd make it. You could do the college good service there, Jeremy."

"I wanted to, sir."

"Maybe gain some fine experience yourself, although I understand Will hasn't much use for college newspapers and thinks they're a waste of time."

"He would."

"But I learned a lot on *The Targum*," Silvers said reflectively. "It brought me close to the college—the whole college. And then it taught me something more—something even the sophomore news editor you met a few minutes ago had to learn. How to take it, Jeremy. You learn taking orders before you can have the right to give them."

Jeremy scowled down at the floor and Silvers found his pipe and lighted it. The twinkle had gone out of his eyes.

"You and I, Jeremy, are both looking for something. We both need it very much—everybody needs it. I wish I could find a better name for it, but let's call it a philosophy of life. You and I aren't going to be happy if we let ourselves get in our own way—sort of stumble over our own spiritual big feet, so to speak. We have to get along—with ourselves, with others. We have to sit up on a hill, sort of, and look down at ourselves, and pick apart the spots we don't like."

Jeremy was thinking that Silvers sounded like his old high school principal; with a wart on his nose Silvers might have looked like the old buzzard, too—

"If you can get the habit of sitting up on that hill, Jeremy, it is going to help a lot. You are going to see above and beyond people—above the things they do, beyond the immediate consequences. You are going to understand them and forgive them and be able to live with them. I'd like to have you try it."

"By going back to *The Targum?*"

"Not that in itself. But now you're low; you're in a valley; you're defeated. Frustrations close in on you; you surround yourself with an armor of defenses; you're all bottled up. Up on that hill you're going to be freer. You're going to be harder to defeat. You're going to be happier."

Jeremy looked across the desk at the man. Silvers was not his high school principal. Silvers was a friend, a good friend.

"Did you ever sweep the floors of the Targum Building?"

"We didn't have a Targum Building all to ourselves in those days."

Jeremy knew what Silvers would have done, though. When he came back into the Targum Building the sophomore news editor had forsaken his mumble-the-peg for a green eyeshield and a yellow copy pencil. Jeremy went to the hall closet and found the broom.

II

In spite of the fact that Jeremy began so poorly, *The Targum* became in large degree the focal point of his college life; here he was to work harder, longer, and with greater satisfaction than he was ever to work at any other enterprise during the ivy years, his studies included. The scuffed floors, the wobbly banisters, the cracked ceilings, and the grimy casement windows of this ancient building were to become fixed forever in his memory; and he was to come to regard with affection the half dozen desks, the four battered typewriters, the rickety tables, the discarded filing cabinet, and the assortment of disreputably decrepit chairs that might have fetched twenty cents at a rummage sale.

The front room on the second floor belonged to the managing editor, who lived there rent free in slightly less filth than filled the other chambers; his was the privilege of using the one bath tub in the building provided he possessed the ambition to clean out the newspapers, cigarette butts, worn-out electrotypes, and empty Coca Cola bottles that invariably collected there. Theoretically the editor-in-chief was over the managing editor, but that colossus seldom was seen, preferring to remain aloof while he collected twenty-five per cent (about $450) of the paper's earnings by writing on such ponderous subjects as keeping off the campus grass or getting out to support that Big Red Team. Otherwise the managing editor was the paper; he could hire and fire, demote and promote; he could decide what stories were to be used, where they were to go in the paper, and how many words were to be consumed in their telling. The Targum Building became his castle to have and to hold except for two days in the year when the members of the Class of 1911 arrived with a Negro flunkey for their annual reunion; then no man's hallowed ground was secure.

The managing editor's name was Price; he was a tall, good-looking chap who dressed well and prosperously; he majored in ceramics and studied industriously; but he had the reputation of being the sort who depended more on a suave manner than on his brain power to get by. Jeremy doubted the charge; suaveness was scarcely the word for Price as a *Targum* freshman came to know him, unless, of course, bobcats and African devil dancers also were considered suave. Happily freshmen received little attention from Price; he walked past them imperiously, his nose in the air, as though he found even the odor of their presence offensive.

"He practices walking like that before a mirror," Abe Lyons told Jeremy. "Everything about Price smacks of a ham actor."

Jeremy laughed. Abe was another journalism major, a roly-poly fellow whose sporty plaid suit and bulging blue eyes made him look like a character out of a Damon Runyon story. "That big boob Price," Abe began again, then lapsed into a grin. "Boob or not, I'd like to be able to strut around like that. It must be wonderful."

Jeremy nurtured the same secret ambition; it was this hope, seeming so desperately far above all of them and yet fated to fall to one of them before the ivy years ended, that made tolerable the abject thralldom they suffered. At the end of a week on *The Targum* Jeremy was already studying his fellow candidates for the staff and calculating his chances against the field. Abe was a definite threat. And the Negro boy, Ted Lawton, whose old man held a newspaper job in Washington, D. C. And Jack Brindle, a curly-headed boy who talked to Price on terms of social equality and who was rated good fraternity material. There were others, too, whom Jeremy knew thus far by face only, but whose continued presence in the Targum Building each Monday and Thursday was proof that they harbored the same fond dreams as he.

Billy Farrand was the sophomore news editor who had set Jeremy to sweeping the floors his first day on the staff. Billy's mouth seemed formed in a perpetual leer, and Abe swore that Billy was hired out every summer to curdle milk in a cheese factory. Billy had prepped at New York Military Academy and knew how to administer discipline; Jeremy could regret with good reason that, by the unspoken pact which existed between the four sophomore editors on such matters, he had become Billy's personal slave.

"You'll do what you're told, too," Billy snarled. "The only future I've got on this paper is riding the pants off you."

"Why pick on me?"

"Because you're a fool like I am. You're a neutral, and a neutral hasn't a chance on this paper. The fraternities run it, boy; we just sit around and take the crumbs."

"Then why do you stick?"

"Because I happen to like it, you stupid ass. Now run this copy down to the printer before I cut your throat with these scissors."

Jeremy went off across the campus, clutching in his hand the copy for the printer. He was filled with sudden sympathy and tenderness toward Billy. Fraternity politics left Billy against a blank wall; the system was stupid and heartless and unfair. Billy was a good newspaper man—a thousand times better than Price—and he deserved a chance to go ahead. Jeremy's mouth tightened. The system wasn't going to trap him as it had Billy. It seemed almost a matter of conditioned reflex any more that when Jeremy was confronted with challenge he grew pugnaciously stubborn.

But back at *The Targum* there were few characteristics in Billy that seemed designed to nourish affection toward him. It was nearly midnight, and Jeremy, weary of typing guest lists for fraternity house parties and of recopying stories too pitilessly blue-pencilled by Billy to be intelligible to a typesetter, appealed to Billy: "How many c's and m's in recommend?"

"Somebody walk home with the dictionary?"

"No, but—"

"Look it up," Bill said curtly. "Learn to spell for yourself."

Across the room Abe Lyons, who had been twice rebuked by Billy that evening for being mentally lazy in checking on his own spelling, smiled sympathetically.

"Another thing," Billy snapped, "while you're there look up words with 'non' before them because you've never learned how to hyphenate them."

Jeremy bit his lip. He'd like to sock Billy good—right in the jaw. He was ten minutes at the dictionary and a perverse streak led him to use a synonym for "recommend" so that when Billy went searching through his copy to see if the word were properly spelled it wouldn't be there at all. But Billy said, not the least offended, " 'Commend' makes more sense in this case. Sometimes you almost seem intelligent."

Billy taught spelling, grammar, and punctuation more compellingly than any member of the English faculty, for he taught from a completely practical basis: either the pupil could learn or surrender the privilege of helping to congest the always overcrowded quarters of *The Targum* newsroom. And principles of composition were taught by Billy more effectively than by most instructors: "Look, it cost money to put type on paper. Tell this story simply, on the same principle that makes a straight line the shortest distance between two points. Get the story organized in your mind before you write—the facts in order of descending importance so that if we have to cut the story in type we can cut from the bottom up. And don't write: 'The scientist *has reached the conclusion* that'; simply say '*concludes*' and save the unnecessary words."

Jeremy struggled to master the rules that Billy laid down, but there was always something more. "Now this story about the guy at the College of Agriculture who has discovered a repellent for mosquitoes that you can make yourself," Billy stormed one day. "This is dull as sin. Did you talk with the guy? How much of the stuff do you mix in a pail of water to make it work? Is the odor offensive? What does it feel like when you rub the stuff on your arms? Get out and see that fellow and pump some human interest into your copy."

"Shall I drink the stuff to see if it'll harm little babies?"

"That's a good news angle," Billy retorted.

Jeremy went off, grumbling. Silvers was paid to write news releases, and he had rewritten the news release Silvers had given him, and still Billy wasn't satisfied. But as Jeremy trudged the mile and a half across town to the campus of the College of Agriculture he was forced to admit that in more respects than one Billy Farrand was among his greatest teachers. Billy was forcing him to higher standards of craftsmanship by sweat and practice, and not alone for any sadistic satisfaction he might derive from cracking down.

"You've got a chance," Billy snarled in his more cheerful moods. "You'll make a good editor. The system's against you, and there's only one way to lick it. By effort. By being so much better that they haven't the brass to turn you aside."

Jeremy answered grimly. He'd stick. He'd measure up to Billy's standards. Deep in his heart he was proud of *The Targum* for the high standards that stemmed from Price and extended to the lowliest freshman underling on the staff. The effort to write with professional flavor was a tradition of the paper; few classrooms could equal the competitive spirit of excellence and sincerity in effort that these student-editors imposed upon themselves and their charges. The tradition itself was kept alive by one simple fact. *The Targum* was read; it exerted wide influence in shaping under-graduate opinion; and derision and ridicule were the sting-ing prices for pulling a bloomer.

During Jeremy's third week on the paper a rather shame-ful mistake crept into page one of *The Targum;* in a direct quote, attributed to the president of the university, a double negative and a split infinitive appeared, obviously errors in grammar placed in the president's mouth by some thought-less freshman reporter. While Jeremy had not been respon-sible for the misquotation, he felt the humiliation of it as he was crowded into the main news room for a meeting of the staff. Billy Farrand spoke first, in his habitual leer, his sentiments as cutting as the steel ruler he pounded on the desk. But Billy's blistering remarks were simply the prelude to the grand orchestration of invective and abuse, for then Price strode into the room. In an idiom derived principally from Anglo-Saxon antecedents Price compared freshman reporters to lice and apologized to any small arachnids or crustaceans or insects that at the moment were occupying the building. He fired the entire staff, sophomore editors included; reconsidered; rehired them all on a probationary status and offered to fight anyone who thought that was funny. In a faded bathrobe, his dark eyes crackling, Price appeared the apostle of truth and the last refuge of decency. Jeremy's spirits shrunk; he kept his eyes on the floor and felt disgust with his fellow reporters for the sin committed; and the only factor that saved him from complete despair was the private opinion that Price was a blowhard who couldn't have won his authority except through fraternity politics.

Price, in many respects a dauntless, conceited fellow, took pride in his reputation as a campus politician; he was a member of Delta Upsilon and never denied that his fraternity controlled *The Targum* in an agreement with Theta Zeta. In an expansive mood one day after he had won eighty cents matching dimes with Abe Lyons, Price summed up his philosophy with succinct cheerfulness: "College is a matter of gypping and being gypped." And Price believed it. The present editor-in-chief was a Theta Zeta, a D.U. was already picked for the post the following year, and after that, of course, the editorship would go back to the Thetes. But Jeremy still hoped for a miracle since Theta Zeta had no freshman pledge among the candidates. The common enterprise, for all its toil and potential heartbreak, could claim numerous light moments—Hamburgers at midnight in Louie's, the publicity-minded profs who brought in news releases that were scornfully mutilated behind their backs, the ballads about the College for Women that were composed night after night and luckily never found their way into print. At such times it was easy to forget the fraternity monopoly over the paper, but the forces at work behind the scenes couldn't be ignored forever. Late in the freshman year Jack Brindle was pledged to Theta Zeta. Gloom descended heavily upon the other freshmen; and only Billy Farrand appeared to retain his courage in the face of the system.

"You've just begun to fight," he told Jeremy.

III

While in so many respects college was an artificial environment set off from the world, there came to the campus a steady procession of the great and the near-great; and like an enormous, fluttery hawk Jeremy prowled the corridors of the upper gymnasium, half sickened by the odor of chlorinated water drifting up from the swimming pool, but determined that whatever the cost no celebrity was to deny him an interview. With minor exceptions what the readers of *The Targum* learned from these interviews was very little, but Jeremy's own education was rounded out in a sense. Back stage, before a lecture or concert, he was exposed to the personality of the visiting dignitary of the moment, and he saw him, so to speak, with rather a worm's eye view. There were those who were gracious and those who were little better than cantankerous children, but Jeremy hounded them all with a brashness of his own, never once possessing the good sense nor the charity of spirit to tell some distraught, half-naked artist that what had been offered to him for a dressing room was in daylight the swimming coach's office and unless he stepped carefully he might have a nasty touch of athlete's foot by which to remember his appearance on the campus.

One Monday afternoon when Jeremy reported to *The Targum,* there was a note on the downstairs bulletin board directing him to see Price. Jeremy climbed the stairs to the managing editor's quarters with a frightened queasiness in his stomach; Price could dismiss him from the staff if the fancy struck him. The freshman entered the sacred room with timidity stretched like a caul across his countenance; but Price appeared no more than ordinarily abusive—he looked up from a textbook, grunted, and at once reburied his nose in the book.

"Paul Robeson's giving a concert in the gym tonight," Price said. "You know that, I hope."

"Yes, sir."

"He's expected on the campus at about four o'clock."

"Yes, sir."

"What do you know about Robey?"

"He's a Nigger."

"Negro—not Nigger," said Price sharply. "Learn to talk like a gentleman. Robey's the greatest man ever to graduate from this place. Class of 1919. He came here from Somerville, a minister's son, and got knocked around by lugs like you who could only think of him as a 'Nigger.' But Robey had guts; he stuck and became Phi Bete, an All-American end, and graduated one of the most popular men in his class. Now he's famous—he's acted and sung in Russia and England—and yet he's not too big for his pants. He's coming back here to sing tonight, and that's a big story. Can you handle it?"

Jeremy wanted to say he had done all right with the Rachmaninoff interview two weeks before, but simply nodded his head.

"Your Rachmaninoff story stank," Price said, as if he had read his mind. "You wrote more about the dancing keys of the piano than about the artist. Give Robey a break."

"Yes, sir," Jeremy said and retreated in contrite confusion. But halfway down the stairs his spirits revived; he had been assigned the lead story and a wonderful sense of importance rose in him.

Silvers was on the phone when Jeremy burst into the office, and snatches of his conversation were intelligible: "Yes, Robey's coming at about four o'clock . . . he's going up to watch football practice . . . no, he never sang on the college glee club . . . never went out for it, I guess. . . ."

Jeremy's mouth suddenly tautened. Dark suspicion smoldered in his mind. Silvers was trying to gloss over the fact that Robey had never sung on the college glee club, but that was nothing better than a press agent's effort to whitewash the college's prejudice against Niggers. Niggers were always getting kicked around, Jeremy thought virtuously as the telephone conversation ended.

At five minutes to four Silvers closed the office so that he could meet Robey at the station, and Jeremy tagged along. Rocky, the head coach, was at the station before them. And then the train came in and Robey stood on the platform surrounded by people from the college. Jeremy watched the great man with envy; Robey was a massive figure, black as coal, whose quick, infectious smile and deep, rich voice seemed to take the bluster out of a chill November day. Robey shook hands, and laughed, and asked after Dickie Morris, who, he said, had been like a second father to him in college. Standing in the background, Jeremy felt pretty silly about the race prejudice suspicions. The President of the United States couldn't have received a more enthusiastic reception.

Jeremy went up to football practice, and Iron Man trotted over to the sidelines. "Let me get one crack at him," Iron Man boasted. "I'll lay him flat."

"Before a concert?"

"Football's football," Iron Man retorted heartlessly.

But Robey was content merely to throw a few passes, and Rocky stood guard at his side. Iron Man surrendered his high hopes, considering the fact that Rocky and Robey were a formidable pair. Silvers called Robey aside.

"I want you to meet a friend of mine, Robey. This is Jeremy Baxter."

Robey shook hands. Jeremy, feeling his fingers virtually pulverized, said hesitantly, "Would you make a statement for *The Targum,* Mr. Robeson?"

"It's good to be home."

"Is that all, sir?"

Robey put his hand on Jeremy's shoulder. "Say anything you want. The happiest years of my life were spent on this old campus. I remember thinking about it one day in Europe, riding on a slow, jerky train. It was raining, and I thought: 'I'd like to be back.' "

Jeremy blurted, "Why didn't you sing on the college glee club, sir?"

"Because I didn't think I'd fit there," Robey said simply.

Jeremy felt suddenly humbled. Here was a great artist who had been acclaimed all over the world and who didn't remember first the snubs, but that an old mathematics professor had been like a second father, and that one rainy day in Europe he had wanted to be back on the campus.

College had been his happiest years, Robey had said—and Iron Man had wanted to lay him flat four hours before a concert. Greatness was only a relative term—the campus was used to seeing it around. Jeremy grinned.

That evening he sat in the gym and listened to Robey sing; in full dress Robey looked different from the Robey he had seen on the football field, but the broad smile and boyish manner were unchanged, the wonderful vibrance of the voice only richer. The audience cheered and rose to its feet; Robey came back for an encore, a second, a third, a fourth; then, a happy, perspiring, exhausted figure, he sang "On the Banks of the Old Raritan." The cheering grew pandemonious. Jeremy, by chance of a backward glance, saw the half dozen Negroes sitting apart high in the gym. Now there was pathos, Jeremy decided sentimentally; there were Robey's own people standing by.

Price read that part of Jeremy's story and looked nauseated. "This is rot—a half dozen Negroes and you've got to be a sob sister! Who said you were a reporter?"

Price knew music. He wrote the piece himself, giving considerable attention to a group of six Russian folk songs Robey had sung. If Jeremy hadn't howled indignantly, Price might have forgotten to mention Robey's rendition of "Old Man River."

Robey went back to New York to open in a new play, and Jeremy read the reviews, remembering Robey's hand on his shoulder. College seemed filled with little incidents like that. And in other similar incidents Jeremy, as the callow, knock-kneed undergraduate reporter, was to absorb an education in music that only a college campus could provide. He watched the Ballet Russe from the wings of the State Theatre and never forgot the facial control of the ballerina as a fly buzzed close to her nose; Jascha Heifitz, sweaty and tired with his fiddle under his arm, received him cordially; Jose Iturbi, on his way to the concert stage, stole a glance at a pretty girl in the audience and smiled to himself (or so Jeremy interpreted the incident). These personalities, and others, as artists, as human beings, were part of the story he reported for *The Targum,* but he never reported it with any deep awareness of its full significance; education in the great liberal arts tradition was being unfolded before his eyes and ears so that his textbooks might become alive, and so that he might have the experience of living intimately with the men and women who vitalized the culture of his generation. What part of this lesson Jeremy gained, he absorbed not directly but rather by a kind of osmosis, and osmosis was difficult in a tuxedo that after only a year was already a size too small. He was more concerned with writing his story against the deadline, and then, proud of his appearance as a man of affairs, to sneak downtown to some open-all-night diner to impress those sleepy habitués who looked up from their morning tabloids to give him a fleeting glance. He believed that he filled them with not a little envy; they suspected that he was some waiter who had just been bounced from a job and no wonder, the silly way he dripped a jelly doughnut over his chin.

Political leaders of all shapes and varieties of ideological coloring came to the campus; Jeremy viewed them all from a distance, aloof and distrustful, for he was a product of the political cynicism that proximity to the Hague machine inevitably produces; perforce he went to chapel once a year to hear the governor of the state supply the pulpit, but his principal reaction to that experience was one of astonishment at the amount of bad poetry he heard recited. On the Rutgers campus as elsewhere Norman Thomas was popular with those students who believed themselves liberal. A kind and elderly man with fine, keen eyes, the great Socialist won respect for his intellectual integrity and for his goodness of spirit. Jeremy sat with him in the home of a professor, needling the poor man for his views on higher education, as though under Socialism he expected to discover some new and painless formula for passing six-week tests; after half an hour he had sense enough to realize that their hostess had taken to watching the clock, and the cook to glaring menacingly through a crack in the kitchen door; Jeremy left at once, realizing it would be a pity if the dinner were spoiled, for Norman Thomas had failed to teach him any great political wisdom. He went away liking the man very much; Norman Thomas was against sin in politics and so was Jeremy.

In later years Jeremy realized that within himself, as within most of his classmates, the ivy years had failed to cultivate political maturity. He came to the campus cynical and contemptuous of American political parties, and he left without the slightest urge to do anything about reforming them. No visiting lecturer, no one of his professors ever succeeded, even if it can be said that he tried, in awakening him to revolt or in appealing to the innate idealism that was still his youthful privilege; his friends who had gone to other colleges and universities were no different from him in this respect—they were all part of the political unconsciousness that was being nurtured in those days. If there was any political impulse rampant on the campus in the years before Pearl Harbor, Jeremy reported it in *The Targum* as the peace movement. Rallies were held and petitions were signed, and Jeremy discovered that he did not favor war any more than he approved of adultery. One day coming back from a peace rally, Jeremy fell in with an elderly professor, a sedate old gentleman who apparently had never uttered an uncouth word in his life; and for a moment Jeremy doubted his own hearing. The old professor swore bitterly.

"I'm pretty sick of being told I fought in the World War to make the munition manufacturers richer or because Woodrow Wilson duped me," the man said. "I fought because my convictions told me that was the honorable thing to do, and luckily my convictions coincided with the will of Congress. These pacifists mean well enough, but they can undermine a country's morale. Did you sign their pledge?"

"Yes, sir."

"That you won't take up arms unless your country's invaded—when it's mighty late to do much about it?"

Jeremy looked down his nose, uncertain of what he had pledged.

The old professor's eyes softened. "Boy, learn to read petitions before you sign them. Read them and think them through. Your signature given on a sheet of paper should signify your will to stand behind it."

Jeremy watched the old professor walking up the path to the Alumni and Faculty House. Jeremy saw himself revealed as something of a fraud, the campus as too readily taken in by fads.

But the university was a restless, changing place, a thing of life and pulsebeat; *The Targum,* as the reflector of all that went on, gave Jeremy little time to philosophize upon his own shortcomings. Within an hour he had forgotten the peace rally, for he was seated in Ballantine Building listening to a debate between Dartmouth and Rutgers. Except for the debaters, the coaches, and the judges, Jeremy was practically the whole audience; he listened for an hour while the pros and cons of the World Court were argued. Jeremy knew, for he had written the story for *The Targum* two weeks before, that more than two hundred undergraduates took part in debating; they toiled for months marshalling the facts on any of a dozen controversial issues of the day and stood ready to argue either the affirmative or negative side of each question; sometimes they broke up into five or six teams and were gone from the campus for a fortnight, travelling hundreds of miles in automobiles and debating twenty or thirty other institutions on a single trip; sometimes they debated over the radio, and thousands of post cards were received from listeners, voting for one team or the other. But the trips into the hinterlands were the big attraction and great tales were told on returning home—of the red-headed gal in a diner in a town in Indiana who had flipped a flapjack so that you'd swear it was going to come down into her bosom; of a little country hotel where in the middle of the night a cow had given birth to a calf under the coach's window; of that time in Washington when one of the boys had asked a waitress where they could find a good hot spot, and they had all gone to the address she had given them to discover that she had sent them to the White House.

Driven by Price and Billy Farrand into giving full measure for his first year and a half of slavery on *The Targum,* Jeremy gained a wisdom of the campus that neither the dean of men nor the president of the university could equal. The campus cops, yes—they knew more than they ever told. Toward ten o'clock, coming back to *The Targum* with the story of some club meeting (history, biology, economics—there was one for every field of interest), Jeremy would hear through the open chapel doors the perspiring glee clubbers singing lustily. When he stopped to listen, as he often did, for there was a lift in well-trained male voices, he might see a boy and girl spooning on the porch of the Alumni and Faculty House; Jeremy would hurry on then—he was rather a gentleman about such things—but for prom week end he remembered the city park that adjoined the campus and wrote a couplet that he thought passably good advice—

> *Buccleuch Park*
> *Is very dark.*

Or coming back from a meeting with the football coaches in the gym where, to Jeremy's way of thinking, nothing had been explained beyond the fact that win, lose, or draw on Saturday the outcome would be no more than the coaches would expect, Jeremy would see the lights on in Student Union and know that Student Council was in session, the staff of the annual at work on page layouts, a group of undergraduates engaged in a game of ping-pong; or he might encounter some fellow freshman nonchalantly leading a horse up onto the porch of the School of Education Building, a forerunner to Hell Week when the fraternities settled down to putting their pledges through the paces. Or coming back from a concert of the University Band (Muggsy, as usual, blew too many sour notes on his clarinet and once was betrayed by his myopia so that he picked up the wrong score of music and began a violent solo that put the audience on the tipsy edges of their chairs, and on the ragged edges of their nerves), Jeremy would hear the rifle team at practice, or he might observe that over on Holy Hill where the seminary was situated a pair of unchristian gentlemen were wending their way homeward with the Pennsylvania Railroad station sign over their shoulders. At such moments Jeremy breathed deeply of the cool, clean air and thought, "This is it. This is college!"

IV

When, halfway through the sophomore year, *The Targum* elections were held and the new staff appointed, Jeremy couldn't sleep for two nights. He had been beaten and kicked around like a nondescript dog for three terms, he had swallowed his pride and suffered a discipline that would have rated fair with the Army, and yet the thought of not making the staff filled him with a growing ache that simply would not go away. He calculated his chances against those of the other candidates and always came off a weak fifth or sixth with only four sophomore editorships to fill—two in news, two in sports. Jack would make the staff—Jack was Theta Zeta now, in line to be editor a year hence. Jeremy was willing to concede that. Surprisingly his sympathy for the Negro that had blossomed into such sweet flower on the day Robey had come to the campus wavered when he thought of Ted. Ted was mighty smart and wrote like a fool. Some of the pulps bought his stuff every month. Ted might make the staff; living by himself in a rooming house on Somerset Street, Ted had worked faithfully on *The Targum*, knowing there was always a prejudice against Negroes on a white man's campus and yet remembering how Robey had risen above it. Ted would not be easy to turn down; freed from the distractions of dormitory life he had worked with a dogged singleness of purpose. His only identity on the campus was *The Targum*. He meant to stick.

Jeremy admitted that Ted was a threat. And there was Abe; and Smoky, an overgrown, awkward, tongue-tied boy, who was one of Price's distant relations—fourth or fifth cousin or something. Jeremy felt defeated and heartsick. He felt like quitting school. But Jeremy had forgotten Earl Reed Silvers, who had a vote on the Targum Council and considerable influence in the elections. Jeremy made the staff.

Jack should have been Jeremy's natural and detested enemy; they were personal rivals now, and the odds were stacked heavily in Jack's favor. But within a week Jeremy had forgotten even that. Jack had become one of his closest, his best friends. Part of the reason was the new managing editor, Bigelow, known to the initiated as Creeper because his trousers had a way of edging down over his buttocks until he resembled a hippopotamus half out of water. Creeper Bigelow was Price with a halo; Creeper liked to live and let live; Creeper couldn't resist being human, even to calling his girl in Panama at *The Targum's* expense on the day he graduated from college. And Creeper was like this: he had come to college without a nickel, and had worked his way through thinking of what a mess it was to be just another mill hand like his old man, and had often gone hungry two or three days at a stretch and on principle wouldn't let anybody treat him to breakfast because it might start a bad habit; and then on the night before commencement he went out and became so gloriously drunk that he all but slept through the graduation exercises and receiving his degree! Creeper had a job with the New Brunswick newspaper, *The Home News,* and that meant he couldn't give as much time to *The Targum* as Price had given, so that making up the paper, which was rightfully his responsibility, fell onto the shoulders of Jeremy and Jack.

Jack was nothing more than a kid compared to Creeper and Price, or even to Jeremy. He was girl-conscious and girl-shy at the same time, outwardly affable and inwardly moody, quick to laugh but as quick to wonder if maybe by laughing someone wasn't being hurt—a constant mixture of head and heart with all the perilous uncertainties such an off-balance can instill within an adolescent. The thing that Jeremy discovered within a week was that Jack, despite his Theta Zeta backing, felt that he didn't have a chance for editor with Jeremy around. It broke his heart in a sense, knowing how the Thetes were depending on him. He tried to cover it up but he couldn't—not from Jeremy.

The Targum was printed in a hole-in-the-wall print shop not far from the campus. The compositor was a lean, lank, sallow-skinned fellow with a lachrymose face who was known to his colleagues as Hell Box, a name derived from the receptacle into which used type is dumped. Hell Box's basic loyalty was not to his craft but to his employer's pocketbook; the more quickly he could slap the type into the chase the greater the profits on the job would be; Hell Box at work was very much like Creeper's trousers, giving the impression that unless he was watched closely he might not be there to watch. Jeremy observed Jack making up the front page and understood at once that he was being shamefully misguided by the artless Hell Box; for the sake of speed the page was entirely out of balance—heads were being placed into the form without any regard to weight value or effective contrast, columns of type were being heavily leaded rather than taking the time to set a few lines of filler, a column rule had been turned over so that when it printed it would appear even blacker than the edges of Hell Box's fingernails. Jeremy could have kept quiet in the hope that Jack's candidacy for editor would be crippled by this demonstration of his incompetency, but Jeremy didn't keep quiet—perhaps out of loyalty to the paper, but more likely out of an instinctive antagonism for Hell Box's slovenly, unimaginative craftsmanship.

Hell Box remonstrated bitterly. If the page were made over as Jeremy insisted, the boss would fire him for time wasted; but Jeremy retorted vindictively that any change in that quarter could be reckoned an improvement. In a very few moments the argument had risen to the brittle, nerve-splitting pitch of a fishmonger's dispute; then from the dim interior of the press room where a Kelly flatbed press operated with the mournful groan of a mortally wounded pachyderm the boss appeared, an agitated little man with ink stains on his undershirt. Every issue he was losing money printing *The Targum;* he was losing money on everything he printed for the college and always there was trouble; if they thought his work was poor, just let them see what they'd get from one of his lousy competitors. Jeremy sneered as years before Price had sneered in much the same situation, and even Hell Box leered somewhat, knowing perfectly well that the boss was earning a good part of a comfortable living out of college printing. But the little man continued to lament his straitened finances; his was an act that every merchant in town performed with adroitness; they were all losing money on the college, and nobody gave them credit for their service to a worthy cause.

"In the old days," the boss said suddenly, "the *Targum* boys used to bring me passes to the football games."

Jack's face brightened. The football manager was a Theta Zeta. The petty graft was agreed upon, an extra pass was thrown in for Hell Box, and the boss consented just this once to permit the page to be remade.

But for Jack his part in the long hours that followed in ensuing weeks as they worked with Hell Box over the composing stone was not a happy one; he brought the passes and Jeremy did the work of supervising. Jeremy was clever at make up; even Hell Box recognized that. His pages had a compactness, a flavor. He insisted on careful spacing, the resetting of bad lines, but Hell Box no longer quarrelled. Jeremy had read books about typography; sometimes Jeremy brought in the late editions of the metropolitan dailies and he and Hell Box looked them over critically, picking up here and there an idea that could be used in *The Targum*. Jack stood around, watching, listening, understanding that Jeremy was awakening Hell Box to an interest in craftsmanship; but Jack could not shake the sense of uselessness that seized him; without his fraternity he wouldn't have a chance for the editorship and a fear was eating into his heart—maybe he wouldn't take the editorship even if he could get it, for Jeremy would know he didn't deserve it. Hell Box would know, too.

One evening walking back from the print shop, Jack said, "You make me feel like an awful heel."

Jeremy glanced up, surprised. He hadn't really paid too much attention to Jack these past few weeks—he had been too happily occupied educating Hell Box.

But ruling the copydesk in the news room was another experience; here Jack and Jeremy were equals with twenty beleaguered freshmen for their vassals, and since Creeper's job with *The Home News* kept him out of the building most of the time, theirs was the responsibility of maintaining discipline.

"Shades of Price," Jack chuckled one day when he had blistered a young hopeful for being late with his copy. "You know, I've gotten so used to saying those Anglo-Saxon words I'm afraid to go home. If I ever slipped, my mom would box my ears without a bit of warning."

Jeremy wondered what Billy Farrand did with his Mondays and Thursdays now that *The Targum* elections had dropped him from the staff. He scarcely ever saw Billy any more, and he missed Billy's barbed tongue. Billy had really deserved to be managing editor, but the system had been too big for him. Even Creeper admitted that.

Compared to Billy, Creeper wasn't a managing editor in the true *Targum* tradition. Creeper was too easy-going for the job, for even if he did enforce discipline, he would feel compelled to make amends by treating the crowd to Cokes, an extravagance he could ill afford. It was probably just as well that no one on the staff saw Creeper until he finished on *The Home News,* and it was usually then past midnight. But Jack and Jeremy waited for him every Monday and Thursday. Creeper sat around in a pair of faded blue pajamas, yawning sheepishly; he never had enough sleep, but he wanted to talk as much as the two sophomores—about himself and the paper and girls.

"When do you study?" Jeremy asked.

Creeper glanced guiltily at the pile of textbooks on his desk. The answer was not often—and certainly not for long.

"Then what's the real sense of being in college, Creeper?"

The managing editor sighed sadly. Looked at in that light there wasn't much sense. His marks were poor. But he was with the kind of people he liked for the first time in his life.

and that counted for something. Silvers was a great guy, and Peterson in philosophy, and Dickie Morris. Just knowing men like that elevated him.

"You know," Creeper said, "sometime I'd like to be so rotten rich I could quit working and come back to college and do it all over again—the right way."

"It wouldn't be the same," Jack said.

"Still, I'd like to try it," Creeper insisted.

But Jeremy was thinking that Creeper wouldn't ever be rich; Creeper wouldn't ever be much different from the way he was now—a fellow who dreamed but trapped himself in a rut while he was dreaming. Creeper had never more than scratched the surface of education; he was affable and lovable, but there was no cultivated depth to his mind. It was touching to see a chap struggle so hard for so very little in the end.

It was past midnight now; beyond the window College Avenue was quiet and deserted, really for the first time since dawn; across the street in Winants a few lights still shone, but not many; and off in the distance—that world so near and yet remote, the town—a dog howled lonesomely.

Creeper, stifling a long yawn this time, said, "It's too bad both you guys can't be editor." Creeper wasn't only thinking that the editor made more money than the managing editor; the editor was automatically a member of Student Council and almost certain to be tapped for Cap and Skull, the senior honorary society.

Jeremy laughed; Jack made some wisecrack about being satisfied to be managing editor if he could make as soft a spot out of it as Creeper had; the bull session ended. Jeremy walked as far as the Theta Zeta house with Jack, then trudged on alone to Hegeman. Campus politics. He'd show 'em. Maybe he'd be something of a campus politician himself. Jeremy wasn't fooling.

5

THE BARBARIANS

I

The sultry summer heat gave no indication of ever letting up. Jeremy loafed in the porch hammock, indolent and discontented as his ears picked up the sounds of summer: the sweet trill of a song sparrow, the insistent buzz of a lawn mower, the tinkling bell of a Good Humor truck. In late May the approaching vacation had seemed the most wonderful anticipation of Jeremy's nineteen years, but now that it was the first day of August he was tired of the vacation. All through July the homesickness had been growing in him—a homesickness for the college. As his foot tapped against the porch rail, his heart skipped over the hills and across the fields to where the Raritan meandered past the red shale bluffs below Hegeman. Pictures he had never suspected he'd remember came back to haunt him: the number of a girl in town scribbled on the wall beside the pay telephone in House Three, the row on row of dingy portraits in the chapel, the battered Ford roadster painted yellow and scarlet that had stood every night behind the Phi Gamma Delta house.

Against the porch rail were piled the books that Jeremy had brought home from college. As July had dragged into August, he had set himself to a definite reading schedule: fifty pages a day. For the first few days he had kept vigorously to his schedule, and one evening had involved mom and pop in an argument about Darwinism; but once he tackled his geology field manual, his interest had wavered. Now he was content merely to blink his eyes drowsily as he contemplated the pile of books. That one in the blue cover stood for Twissy —Twissy who lit a cigar when class ended and said, "Nobody ever wept when one of my lectures was over." And the book in the green cover stood for Burns—the big bum who had asked over a hundred questions on final exams. Jeremy yawned. In high school teachers were taken for granted, but it wasn't that way in college. In high school class periods were given over to recitation—day after day the teacher checked to make certain you had read your assignment—but in college nobody cared if you kept up with your work. The profs lectured and you listened; every six weeks there was a test and at the end of the term a three-hour final examination. But Jeremy didn't want to change the system. He just wanted to be back—at Louie's where everybody was "dollink" to Mrs. Louie, at Hegeman where the roar of the showers at quarter after eight in the evening indicated that Iron Man had come back from football practice, at the gym to swim naked in the pool and to sting Muggsy's buttocks with the end of a wet bath towel.

Two weeks before, he had ridden to Newark in a hot bus to spend the day with Iron Man. It had been fine seeing Iron Man again, hearing him talk about girls and football—but mostly football. Iron Man was going back to New Brunswick a week early for training camp; this year Iron Man was supremely confident of winning his varsity letter. As Jeremy had waited for the bus home, Iron Man had confessed that he had pledged Beta Theta Pi and wouldn't be back in Hegeman this fall. Jeremy had felt disconsolate: the old gang was breaking up; the past was dead. And then Visch had come out for a visit. Jeremy had been delighted to see Visch; for old time's sake he had tried to start an argument on religion, but Visch had demurred. Visch was preoccupied with the fact that he had been given another chance at Columbia Dental School and that this time he had to buckle down and make good. Jeremy had agreed but his heart had been heavy. The old Visch was lost, not to the Betas like Iron Man, but to the serious realm of professional school.

Jeremy stopped swinging in the hammock. How he'd like to see Muggsy or Creeper! How he'd like to hear the chatter of voices in *Targum* on a Monday or Thursday night! He remembered that there were a number of old copper engraving plates in the closets in *The Targum* newsroom and wondered if some junkman would pay ten bucks for the lot. He'd have to speak to Creeper about that; they could both get carfare to Easton for the Lafayette game. In another moment Jeremy was asleep; a fly buzzed over his head and the sweat oozed out of his pores. But when he awoke he felt disturbed. He had dreamed that Jack had become editor of *The Targum* and that through a fraternity deal Jack had been forced to drop him from the staff. Jeremy tried to scoff at the fear, but he couldn't escape an undercurrent of uneasiness. It could happen!

A week passed. The danger came back to trouble Jeremy in unguarded moments. He fought it, but there it was just the same. And then toward mid-August while browsing through the public library, his eyes fell upon a history of Tammany Hall. He skimmed through a few pages and, fascinated, carried the book home. He was enthralled by the patterns of connivance and intrigue revealed in the pages of this astonishing book; he read steadily, afternoon and evening, pausing now and then to gaze up at the cloudless sky while he clucked his tongue against his cheek; when at length he finished the book, he saw himself in a new light and in a new rôle—a campus politician according to the Tammany formula.

After that each August day became endless.

II

If you are going to hunt game, Tammany's Boss Tweed once said, hunt it big; and Jeremy followed the old scoundrel's counsel. Dr. Metzger, dean of men, received Jeremy cordially, although not without a note of skepticism, for the dean had learned that golf and boys were much the same— every stroke, every boy represented a new risk with the consequences entirely unpredictable. A shrewd man approaching his three score years and ten, the dean knew boys with the insight of a father who had reared three sons. He suspected that the undergraduates enjoyed pulling the wool over his eyes and was not above letting them try it to see how far they would go. Boys came to him when they were broke, and he loaned them money or awarded them scholarships. Now and then an undergraduate went off to Princeton before a football game to paint that lovely old town a Rutgers scarlet, or frightened some poor spinster out of her wits by dropping a live pig through her bedroom window during Hell Week, and the dean intervened with the local constabulary and bailed the unhappy miscreant out of jail. At other times a boy who had been stricken by the death of a parent, or crushed by failure in his studies, or tricked by his faith in humanity came to the office, and then the dean closed the door and tried to talk to the boy as a father. Whenever his door opened, it could mean adventure or heartbreak—the dean of men could never be sure which.

Jeremy struck the dean as adventure. The boy possessed a fine pair of eyes—splendid eyes really, deep brown, intelligent. And a chin that he had seen once before and had never forgotten, for it was the kind of chin that Woodrow Wilson had carried. When Jeremy began to talk the dean listened, at first with a slightly quizzical frown and then respectfully. Dr. Metzger admitted that the nonfraternity man was cheated out of part of his college life as a result of not having an organized program of social activities. If Jeremy could organize such a program the office of the dean of men would stand behind him, and if the enterprise shaped up well there was no reason why Student Council couldn't appropriate a hundred dollars to help with the expenses.

"But keep out of campus politics," the dean said. "That situation's bad enough and you fellows will only make it worse."

"Yes, sir," Jeremy agreed, "the situation's bad." If Jeremy's comment implied that he had no political aspirations his conscience troubled him very little; like Price the dean was a D.U. and therefore cut from the same piece of cloth; and the knowledge that the dean once had run for the governorship of Vermont on the old Bull Moose ticket convinced Jeremy that the man was not only a political manipulator, but also not a very good one since he had been defeated.

Jeremy had no thought of simply opposing the D.U.'s; he wanted to blast them, along with Theta Zetas, into ignominious impotency. As he saw the situation, all of the fraternities together couldn't marshal the strength of a solidly organized nonfraternity group; and the fraternities couldn't stand together for they were weakened from within with seven or eight small combines, each trading with the other and jockeying for campus dominance. Jeremy felt exalted; he was Tammany's Boss Tweed burning the records before an investigation and Tammany's Fernando Wood plotting to have New York City secede from the Union during the Civil War. The future stretched before him rosily.

That night behind closed doors in Hegeman seven other nonfraternity men, representing the principal living groups on or near the campus, convened at Jeremy's invitation. With the exception of Muggsy Jeremy regarded his guests as strangers and was only impressed by two—Robert Hare, a thin-boned boy with sensitive eyes who lived with the theologs over on Holy Hill, and Duncan Faust, a tall, splindly classmate from an upstate town, whose father was a road gang boss and was openly contemptuous of a son who couldn't lift five pounds of sugar without groaning. Jeremy reckoned it a stroke of good luck that this was a Tuesday evening, since that was fraternity meeting night and Hegeman was cleared of the "enemy"; but as he faced his audience his confidence almost failed him. Somewhat apathetically the seven guests listened to Jeremy's plan for the creation of the Barbarians (as opposed to the Greeks, as the fraternity men were known collectively); but their interest became whetted as Jeremy recited how the dean wanted to keep them out of campus politics. Muggsy, an inveterate snooper, discovered the chocolate cake that Jeremy had received from home that afternoon, and Faust cut it with a steel-edged ruler. Muggsy continued snooping and uncovered a partially filled jug of cider. Jeremy watched this raid on his cupboard with gradually warming spirit; Muggsy's gluttony was a practical demonstration of how to infuse life into the Barbarians.

"We'll feed 'em," Jeremy said. "Look, we'll start with the idea of the Tammany district club, only we'll call 'em social clubs. We'll have one in every dorm, and once a month each club will hold a smoker with a speaker and refreshments. Each dorm club will elect a representative to a central Barb Council and the council will decide policies, draw up tickets at election time, and cover up with the old dean by throwing dances that will be of general interest. It'll work as long as you feed 'em."

"What'll you feed 'em with?" Hare asked.

"With the hundred bucks the dean promised us!"

"I approve of that," Duncan Faust said. "I approve of eating up anything that isn't nailed down in this college to make up for that general fee they tack onto your term bill."

The meeting adjourned to Louie's on Somerset Street. Muggsy drank a milk shake, but it mixed badly with the cider and he dashed out, sick. Jeremy, launched that evening as a campus politician, walked as far as Holy Hill with Robert Hare.

"I hope this idea grows," Hare said. "I hope we can hold a dance soon."

"You got a girl you want to bring?"

"Her name's Margery. She models for an advertising company and makes more dough than I ever will. I see her every week end when I go home."

"It's that serious?"

"That's not the only reason I go home. You see, my mother and father are both blind."

Jeremy suddenly felt embarrassed, as though he had been snooping into something that was none of his affairs. Hare seemed to be acting strangely, for he had stopped and was leaning his back against a tree.

"Wait a moment," the boy from Hertzog said. "I guess I forgot to tell you. I'm supposed to have a bum heart, and I have to watch it."

"What happens?"

"I feel dizzy for a moment, then I'm all right."

"Maybe you ought to sit down."

"No. I'm fine now. Say, isn't it pretty out here under the moon and the stars?"

Jeremy liked Hare. He had found a friend who made him see that there were lots of afflictions worse than his. Hare's bad heart, for one; those two old blind people living together. Or even Muggsy's lack of good sense in just cramming any old slop into his stomach.

One detail in the history of Tammany Hall had escaped Jeremy's notice; while the political bosses only harried the voters to support them on primary and election days, the bosses were forced to work at their jobs seven days a week. Disconcertingly Jeremy discovered that if he wanted to be certain each detail of organizing the Barbarians was carried through, he could attend to it himself; before he finished he had arranged the smokers for each of the seven living groups, had engaged the speakers, and had bought the refreshments. Between launching the Barbarians and toiling on *The Targum* his studies were going to pot, and that worried him; not unlike Creeper's books his books were gathering dust on his desk. But even though scholastic hazards loomed ahead, he clung to his determination to beat Price's crowd at their own game. Luck favored him in his first choice of a speaker. The University physician told the boys a few blunt facts of life, and his talk became campus gossip by morning. Jeremy was no fool; when he moved his smoker to another living group, the University physician went with him and the attendance increased; by the time the swing around the seven groups had been completed the University physician was a tired, hoarse man, the Barbarians had become a campus fixture, and Jeremy had gained a considerable knowledge of venereal diseases.

Although the hundred dollars that the dean of men had appropriated from Student Council funds was gone within three months, Jeremy could look that gentleman in the eye and feel that he had rendered honest service for every penny spent. Before the creation of the Barbarians the nonfraternity man had been in many respects a lone wolf; his intimate friends were few, five or six at most, and more likely two or three; in addition, he had a nodding acquaintance with those men who attended the same classes as he, but there was seldom any real depth in those contacts, and unless he took part in some extracurricular activity like *The Targum* or played on one of the teams there was little opportunity for his breaking through the shell that isolated him. But Jeremy's smokers brought all these men together and awakened a new community of interest. Even Jeremy for a time lost sight of the political force that the Barbarians were intended to represent, and might have been willing to forget it entirely if he had not believed that by so doing he would have been

hoodwinked by the old dean whom he had meant to hoodwink.

A fortnight later Queen's Players, the undergraduate dra-
matic society, announced a talent search; a "Skit Night" was
to be held in the gymnasium for living groups wishing to
compete for a silver loving cup. Muggsy said, "We can win
that and put the Barbarians on the map. I've got an idea.
We'll put new words to Gilbert and Sullivan tunes and
lampoon campus personalities. Say, now you just wait—"
Muggsy broke off to scribble on the back of an envelope.
"Here's one, to the tune of 'I am the Captain of the King's
Navee' in *Pinafore*—

> "*I am the captain of the football team,*
>   *And a right good captain too,*
>   *And though it's often said*
>   *Our team is the Big Red*
>   *We sometimes make you blue;*
>   *Though reputedly a ham*
>   *I have gotten where I am*
>   *Despite my awful play*
>   *You think that I'm a brute*
>   *But I look cute in a suit*
>   *And I never, never play for pay—*"

Jeremy interrupted excitedly. "That's the part in *Pinafore*
where it goes:

> "*Chorus: What never?*
>   *Captain: No, never!*
>   *Chorus: What never?*
>   *Captain: Well, hardly ever!*"

"It's a natural. Let's write the show together."

Jeremy nodded. Within a week the script was completed
and rehearsals were held in Robert Hare's room. Hare, sitting on the desk with a book on ballet dancing on his lap,

endeavored to train the chorus in simple dance routines. He possessed rather a knack for this business, but the odds against him were insuperable. It was not bad enough that Muggsy stepped on any feet within a range of three yards, his own included; Hare's roommate was a sullen, dark-eyed, unpleasant boy named Olanski who protested violently upon this intrusion of his privacy. Olanski spoke English with the heavy accent of a Bulgar; any contact with people upset him tremendously; and to the best of anyone's knowledge he did not have a single friend in college. Hare suspected that Olanski was the kleptomaniac who had been preying on the fraternities and dormitories in recent weeks, but had no proof; he knew that Olanski was an orphan, and he had rather a sympathy for the strange chap; he had known occasions when Olanski had studied steadily from sunset to dawn, and then in the morning, drawn of face, his eyes bloodshot with strain, had angrily thrown all his books onto the floor and stomped out of the room. He would be gone all day. Accustomed to his roommate's idiosyncracies, Hare simply shrugged when Olanski orated; he went on with the rehearsals as though his roommate had never existed, and there was rarely a scene to equal those rehearsals—Hare on the desk, Muggsy out of step, Jeremy prompting from a script pocked with cigarette burns, Olanski leaning against the wall, his lip sucked in until he appeared to snarl.

Six-week tests were drawing near, but they were too deeply committed now to worry. "We need something in this show that'll wow 'em," Hare said. "Muggsy, can't you do something on Prexy to the tune of 'A Wandering Minstrel, I'?"

"Do you think I should?"

"Why not? College presidents are a dime a dozen—every college has one. We ought to do that number right. I tell you, Jeremy, you go to Prexy's wife and borrow that gray salt-and-pepper suit he likes so much."

"You'll get me bounced from school for this."

"Well, be willing to sacrifice something for your art!" Hare and Muggsy set to work on the new number. Hare pounded his foot to give the time of the melody, and Muggsy chewed a pencil and stared up at the hot water pipe. If Hare really had a bad heart, Jeremy thought, he didn't let it spoil his fun.

There was never a doubt about the Barbarians winning "Skit Night" from the moment Duncan Faust shuffled onto the stage as the football captain. And as Hare had predicted, the finale "wowed 'em"—with the possible exception of the president everyone enjoyed the sight of that salt-and-pepper suit rolling around the stage floor while Muggsy sang in a wavering tenor voice:

> *A wandering Prexy, I,*
> *A thing of Trustees meeting,*
> *Of Chapel prayers repeating,*
> *And dream—me-e lullaby . . .*

The dean of men awarded Jeremy the cup and walked home with his arm around the boy's shoulders.

"I like what you're doing, Jeremy."

"Thank you, sir."

"You might have tried being nothing more than a campus politician, and then where would you have been?"

"I daresay not very well off, sir," replied Jeremy, suspecting that he was being needled.

They stopped in front of the dean's house, and the man's eyes twinkled as he puffed on his pipe. "Of course that could come later," the dean said.

Jeremy met the man's glance and the dean chuckled. They understood each other thoroughly.

III

The success of the Barbarians in winning "Skit Night" was a victory that Jeremy quickly put behind him, and with good reason. Between his work on *The Targum* and his ambitions to become a campus politician he had come dangerously close to the point of failure in some of his courses, and there was nothing he could do now but buckle down and render a more creditable performance. In his second year with Twissy he was doing considerably better, and had advanced from a "3" to a "2" student, a difference of ten percentage points in his final grade. Twissy's sophomore course in American literature was surprisingly easy sailing, chiefly for the reason that a four-dollar textbook succeeded in making the subject painless by extracting "typical selections" from the works of Bradford, Mather, Sewall, Cooper, Thoreau, Emerson, and others of the American literary giants. In his sophomore year Jeremy had not yet acquired either the intellectual depth or the intellectual purpose to understand fully the great betrayal that had been foisted upon the students of literature by the compilers of such anthologies. He did not see himself as the victim of a conspiracy between hit-and-run teaching and catchpenny publishing which filled his head with tidbits, snatches, and fragments scarcely worth the effort of retaining; and if the literature of a nation could atrophy through disuse under such commercialized dilletantism, the crime rested lightly on Jeremy's mind since the responsibility for it rested not at all upon his conscience. Twissy must have recognized the danger and struggled to combat it, for some spark of his lectures smoldered on in Jeremy's consciousness and led him in later years to re-read Cooper and Thoreau and Emerson and Hawthorne and Whitman, among others, with at least the tentative respect of trying them by entire volumes. But as a sophomore American literature was at best a shadow to Jeremy as a course in English literature, similarly taught by the tidbit method, was a shadow to Muggsy, and as the freshman course in contemporary civilization had become in the end a shadow to both of them.

And yet a strange urge often imposed itself upon Jeremy

—an urge to intellectual exploration which had no connection whatever with the requirements of his curriculum. Halfway through his sophomore year he found himself in posssession of an impressive number of notes on abnormal psychology that he had dug out for himself from a book Visch had passed on at the end of the previous term. Jeremy simply had started reading the book and had grown despondent at the fact that his memory had not retained more of it; the notes, carefully typed in outline form, constituted a conscientious effort to aid his own voluntary studentship. In the last analysis the notes availed him little; he both read and forgot quickly, a discouraging set of circumstances; and convinced that he was of rather low caliber mentally, he reconciled himself to a humble acceptance of that discovery. But a course in introductory psychology, part of his prescribed sophomore curriculum, came to the relief of his injured dignity. He approached the course with some distaste, for, as in the case of geology his freshman year, it was divided between lecture periods and a weekly two-hour lab session so that week after week there were experiments to write up in the dry, unimaginative tradition of the scientific method. But the lab sessions wisely made the student both the experimenter and the subject of the experimentation; thus by exploring such phenomena as the mechanics of memory and recall, Jeremy came to understand the nature of his own learning curve—that it rose and fell rather like the graph of the day's trading on the stock exchange; that learning was in no sense a constant factor but might very well depend, as the old Chinese philosophers believed, on the condition of the bowels; that the brain as an ingenious device required automatic rests and saw that it got them; that a fact little used was a fact easily forgotten since it formed no graphic association in the conscious mind; that study was more profitably pursued in short periods of concentration with deliberate respites between. That there could be a definite physiological basis to effective studentship was something all his other instructors had failed to point out to him.

"That's the trouble with those birds," he growled to Muggsy. "Anything practical like that they keep to themselves."

"If they know it," Muggsy said cynically.

Jeremy tried seriously to apply to the task of studentship the knowledge he gained of how his own brain functioned, and told himself that the practice helped. By experiment in introductory psychology he tested his own powers of recall by writing down series of numbers, letters, and nonsense syllables as they were flashed before his eyes; he did better than Muggsy or Iron Man in every case. In other experiments he tested his own reading span, the number of words his eyes would take in naturally at a glance, the number of "jumps" his eyes required in reading various lengths of printed lines, and from these tests he learned that a definite correlation existed between the speed at which he read and the amount of what he absorbed from his reading. Nothing could have encouraged him more than the discovery that in most of his sensory perceptions he was well within the norm, and in some respects a bit above. His confidence was shamelessly bolstered by this revelation; his whole approach to study became better natured, even tinged with a note of eagerness. Nothing in the task of studentship seemed beyond his physiological limits if he cared to try.

Still, the borderline courses remained. The first term of modern European history was taught by a sandy-haired, thin-boned, soft-spoken graduate student from Princeton whose self-consciousness before his class was both obvious and painful. Jeremy, with the shrewdness and the instinct that the immature student often manifests in such cases, gambled on the fellow to be soft as his German instructor had been soft his freshman year; he cut class at least once a week, studied indifferently, was inattentive to lectures. The young graduate student, whose name Jeremy never learned, faced his class with rather a thin-lipped uncertainty; he knew that he was being treated with schoolboy impudence, and not by Jeremy alone. At times there was a dangerous flash in his eyes, a flicker of fire that lingered as he waited for some minor disturbance to pass over, some too lusty guffaw to fade away, but then the fire would die down, the lecture would continue, the quiet, really pleasant tone of his voice would resume. The first six weeks' test approached and the young graduate student failed to give one. Jeremy simply chuckled; the fellow was mush, a degree worse than soft. And then Jeremy received his first marking period report—a flat "6," as low as he could receive. He stormed into the instructor's office.

"You have no basis for this!"

"I think I have."

"You may think you have to mark somebody down, just to make it look good, but why pick on me?"

"I didn't pick on you, Baxter. I marked down seventeen out of twenty-one in this class."

"You what!"

"Seventeen out of twenty-one. There was no sense giving you a test, either. I know the game you've been playing and I'm not going to waste my time marking your stupid papers."

"Yeah, but—"

"If I have to I'll flunk all seventeen at the end of the term. It's not a glorious way to start a teaching career, but at least it's honest."

"Yeah, but you could have cracked down."

"I have cracked down."

Jeremy looked the fellow over; there was a deepening respect in his eyes. "This is a dirty trick," he said.

"Do you feel you've treated me as a gentleman?"

Jeremy told him honestly, "I didn't think you cared. After all, it's just a class to you."

The instructor shook his head. "That's where you're

wrong. It's just one more class to you, not to me. I want to teach. I'm going to teach all my life, but not like a blating fishmonger who has to browbeat his students into respect. Teaching means too much to me for that."

"I see, sir."

The young graduate student smiled to himself at Jeremy's sudden use of "sir." "Everything you've had your first six weeks will be on your exam at mid-year, Baxter. You better bone up on it."

"Yes, sir."

"You've been acting like a high school kid, Baxter. Grow up and get in college."

"I'll try."

"And I'll try to grow up with you into a good teacher. You see, I believe in what I'm doing in this class. You'll have to believe in what you're doing and you'll get by in this course —maybe better than you expect."

Upon reflection Jeremy decided that he had not done too well in the interview. He had been a fool; his bluff had been called; all the time he had wasted remained to be made up. But he respected the young graduate student. The guy would make a good teacher.

Jeremy continued to wonder about the young graduate student—in a broader sense, about teaching. Why did a man go into teaching, giving over his life to a succession of brats? Why did Twissy teach; and Syd Sanderson, who always looked half puffed out and bogged down like a pack horse with all the gadgets he carted into class to illustrate his lectures in psychology; and Burns and that fiery-tempered rascal in freshman mathematics and all the other fat guys and skinny guys and plumb-in-between guys who made up a college faculty? But the young graduate student had answered his question—"I believe in what I'm doing." The young graduate student had put right up to him the obligation a student owed his teacher—"You'll have to believe in what you're doing." Faith. Dignity. A sense of rightness. Pop and mom making sacrifices for his education and he trying to take advantage of an instructor's suspected immaturity. That was kid stuff, all right. That was being a first class heel.

General economics, another sophomore course, was different, however. Jeremy knew from the first day there wasn't going to be any nonsense tolerated. Again he studied under a man whose name he was never to learn; he was a dark-skinned chap with deep black hair and bushy eyebrows; Jeremy judged the man to be in his late thirties, which was old enough by Jeremy's standards. The fellow cracked his knuckles and talked on and on and never smiled. Every Saturday morning he gave a quiz, and read the *Wall Street Journal* while the class moaned. His quizzes, however, were not based on his lectures but on the assigned reading; the textbook was just another series of facts set down on paper with sufficient repetition to make known at the end of the chapter what had been dozed over in the preceding pages; Jeremy religiously studied the last two pages of every chapter and no more.

"The stuff is dull," he confided to a classmate, "and I'm not going to do a lick more work than I need to do to pass. If I know six out of ten answers every quiz, I can write those down, make out I haven't had time to finish, and get at least a '4,' which will squeeze by."

"They make you read two textbooks in this class next term."

Jeremy simply calculated that reading four pages of text instead of two would require another fifteen minutes of preparation every week.

In a degree his determination to give general economics no more than the minimum attention necessary to pass the course was evidence, even if negative, that his sophomore year was beginning to bring him some maturity of judgment as a student. Teaching was filled with tricks, but so was learning. If a course was mostly all shadow, like American lit, then it had to be taken for what it was—a smattering of everything but not much of anything. The very nature of the learning curve was against holding on to too much of it. A course like general economics was worth just exactly what you wanted to give it, and you made the choice. And modern European history—but there Jeremy knew he was licked; he would bone over that course; there was a matter of self-esteem involved.

Muggsy said, "You ought to take public speaking. Whenever you want to pass a speech, you just get up and spout off about the great benefit to be derived from going out for debating. Prof Reager likes that."

"Who told you so?"

"Creeper."

Jeremy broke into a grin. Trust Creeper to know all the tricks. Creeper had developed a genius for just getting by— by an eyelash.

IV

Creeper's deepening affection for Jeremy was neither logical nor easily explicable; they saw each other but rarely and then usually toward midnight when Creeper, returning from his job on *The Home News*, talked sleepily of his family and the affairs of the day; but even on such slight nourishment their friendship grew. Creeper was a member of Tau Kappa Epsilon, but he seldom was seen at the chapter house. Jeremy never suspected that he was the cause of the coolness that had come between Creeper and his fellow Tekes; but Creeper had proposed Jeremy for membership in Tau Kappa Epsilon, had seen him blackballed on the basis of his physical disability, and had walked out of the meeting with an anger that never completely subsided. Creeper knew—again something that Jeremy never suspected—that Jack had proposed Jeremy for Theta Zeta but had not brought the nomination to a vote because the same feeling existed. Creeper shook his head, baffled.

"I'd say Jeremy was doing all right with his Barbarians behind him," Jack commented.

"That doesn't make it up entirely," Creeper said.

Iron Man agreed with Creeper. "Jeremy's good fraternity material. I'd like to see him Beta. He's got a chance to be editor of *Targum*, and that would add prestige to the house."

"What's against him?"

"His trouble eating. His aggressiveness, too—he carries a chip on his shoulder at times, and even if it is in self-defense it's held against him. Then he's sloppy personally—dirty fingernails, going all day without a shave."

"It's hard for him to shave or clean his own nails."

"Well, he ought to try."

"You want to tell him?"

Iron Man shook his head. "I'd be willing to take him as he is. The house could bat those habits out of him. But it's harder now that he's started his Barbarians. That's kind of thumbing his nose at all of us."

"He's got a good idea," Creeper said. "I only hope he doesn't solidify sentiment against him so that the fraternities go after him next *Targum* elections."

"He'll have to run that risk," Iron Man said. "In some ways it's too bad, but you know the system."

Creeper was tired of the silly system, but Iron Man, going on down College Avenue, stood loyally by the fraternities. Going through the buffoonery of Hell Week had nearly broken his desire to be a Beta, but Hell Week was behind him now and that fact made a big difference. He had earned his right to belong. Looking back, the one torment in Hell Week that had almost licked him hadn't been the paddling, or being dumped on a lonely country road at two in the morning and told to get to his eight o'clock class as best he could, or going out to steal one of the prize chickens at the

College of Agriculture, or having to wear a chamber pot for a hat and to eat his meals from the same vessel—stew, milk, spinach, potatoes, pie, coffee, and sugar all poured in at once. The dirtiest trick had come the last evening of Hell Week after they had promised him one good meal. Dry cornflakes and cocoa! Iron Man's stomach could still contract at the memory of that concoction. It had been terrible. He hadn't been able to get it down his throat. The stuff had just stuck there, ready to come up again, and his abdominal muscles had begun to ache.

But next day the Beta alumni had come back for the initiation banquet. All through the day Iron Man had felt a sense of anticipation growing in him; there had been something in the air, a change. Some of these Betas of other classes had travelled from far places; one had ridden on the train all night. During the formal ceremony Iron Man had awakened all at once to the pleasant discovery that he was in the presence of older men, not as a boy who was patronized and tolerated, but as a Beta who was accepted on a basis of equality. Something in Iron Man suddenly had been released; he had felt grown up and entirely a man; his initiation banquet had become one of the richest moments of his youth. To the outsider, even to the pledge, the meaning of fraternities might be obscure to that moment. But the knowing made the difference. To Iron Man Beta came first; and it was too bad about Jeremy.

At the moment Jeremy's heart toward Beta and the other houses on the campus could not have been stormier if he had been forced to subsist on dry cornflakes and cocoa. One reason why many nonfraternity men were passed by during the rushing periods was the fact that nobody knew anything about them; but the activities of the Barbarians provided an opportunity for these men to demonstrate qualities of leadership. Within a single week three of the seven men who sat with Jeremy on the policy-making Barbarian Council received bids to fraternities. All three accepted, Robert Hare among them. Jeremy faced the crisis, staggered; this was a blow, perhaps a mortal one, at the very heart of the political dynasty he was seeking to create; in all his scheming here was a possibility with which he had neglected to reckon. The three resignations were received in cold silence; Jeremy adjourned the meeting, feeling betrayed and distrustful of his own emotions; no one needed to tell him that the future of the Barbarians stood in jeopardy, for unless the central council held together, the individual living group clubs would neither long endure nor represent any power politically.

Of the three men who had resigned, Robert Hare alone waited for Jeremy. He was ill at ease under Jeremy's peevish frown, but there was a forthrightness about Hare that made him want the record clear.

"Suppose one of the good houses had offered you a pledge pin, could you have turned it down?"

"Yes, I could. I've got to stand by the cause."

"You and Olanski and the Great Cause!" Hare smiled. "Maybe you would have turned it down, but would you have wanted to?"

"Well," Jeremy began belligerently, "I—"

"I thought not," Hare said softly. His mood became more cheerful.

Jeremy often kidded himself, but tonight he couldn't. He knew Hare too well. Hare's home life had not been altogether normal, and rooming with Olanski could give a guy the creeps. And then there was Margery, a girl anybody would want to take to a fraternity house party. Hare could gain much from a fraternity.

"I think I would have taken it," Jeremy said.

Hare stopped, gazing with sudden embarrassment up the cobbled driveway of Holy Hill. Here was where they parted; he wished that he had a flair for holding out his hand, for saying "Thanks, old man," but that kind of stuff soured him.

Honesty was a trust that made him feel sadly grown up; he didn't even want to look at Jeremy.

"Don't brood over it."

"Who says I will?"

"I do," Hare said. "I did."

Jeremy went on alone down College Avenue. A gibbous moon hung lazily in the sky, and around him the tall old trees seemed forsaken and melancholy. Across the street lights gleamed through the windows of Chi Psi lodge; there was an air of magnificence about the rambling, white-brick building with its verandah running the full length of the structure. Jeremy remembered being inside Chi Psi lodge; he remembered the panelled dining room, the living room where a radio had played and two undergraduates had been stretched on the floor reading *Esquire*. He remembered spring week ends, the girls in their party dresses laughing on the porch, the thump, thump, thump of the drum in the orchestra, the cars coming in and out of the parking lot in back.

He remembered also the evening he had gone to the Delta Upsilon house for his initiation into the Peithossophian Literary Society. Creeper had proposed him for membership, and he had paid three dollars for a Peitho key and three dollars more for a watch chain to wear it on. The meeting had been held in the basement recreation room; he had eyed the pool table enviously, wishing he could have felt at ease staying afterward to play a game as some of the others did, but they were fraternity men and he felt an outsider. Price had appeared as he was leaving and had insisted that he stay, but Jeremy had not stayed, still oversensitive, still feeling an outcast. He went out the door, noting the little things that set a fraternity apart as a highly personalized community: the letters on the table in the hall; the memo tacked to the bulletin board, "Metzger, call your old man"; the quick glimpse through the living room door of the glowing logs in the fireplace. He had gone on into the night, lonely, unhappy, excluded. His Peitho key had become just one more trinket; what good was a literary society where nobody wanted to talk about anything more literary than football?

Jeremy sighed. Hare had told him not to brood, and he wasn't. He was thinking, that was all. Being honest. There were good fellows among the nonfraternity men, and some punks who made fraternities, but on the average the fraternities had the pick. And in an outfit like the Barbarians you ran into guys who made you tighten up, not because you were a snob, but because you didn't like guys who had no concept of simple courtesy. Guys who talked too loud; who were rude at the table; who brought the wrong kind of townies to dances; guys like the mole on the first floor of Hegeman freshman year, spreading their newspapers all over the shower room floor. Jeremy felt defeated and lost, but at the same time a stubbornness crept into his heart. He guessed he had a chip on his shoulder where fraternities were concerned; he was pugnacious and resentful because he was sure that he missed so much.

Creeper came in early the following night; in the second floor front room of Targum Building the managing editor talked straight.

"What do you care if three of your council members resigned to accept pledge pins? They're making your lousy political machine for you. Get smart, Jeremy. Go out and find three more to take their places—find a dozen more if you need to. Show that you're three or four deep in good men wherever you turn, for you've got more than half the student body to pick from."

Jeremy knew this was sound, workable advice. He thanked Creeper warmly, but Creeper performed one of the rare acts of his life—he gave his trousers an upward tug, then took another hitch in his belt—and looked half-disgusted. Jeremy had a sense of estrangement, but it passed quickly—Creeper's trousers had begun sliding.

With the spring came class elections. Jeremy sought out Creeper once more.

"If I'm going to do it, Creeper, it's now or never."

"Do what?"

"Prove that the Barbarians are a political power!"

Creeper hesitated; after all, he was a fraternity man, and to aid and abet this kid was betraying what Iron Man called "the system." Then to devil with the system, Creeper told himself rebelliously; the system had given him the managing editorship of *The Targum* over Billy Farrand, but to this day he couldn't look Billy in the eye without feeling like a cheat. If he hadn't needed so desperately the rent-free living quarters in Targum Building that went with being managing editor, Creeper believed that he might have been man enough to step aside in favor of Billy. Sometimes he wished that he had stepped aside, anyhow; what was the sense of going through college if all you accumulated were a series of small regrets—that you had studied more faithfully, that you had lived better, that you had done the fair thing even if it cost you a hundred bucks extra room rent?

Creeper looked at Jeremy's worried face and smiled. A kid with spunk. Creeper, well aware of his own easy-going nature, admired backbone in others. He'd like to see Jeremy beat the fraternity crowd. Campus politics was nonsense if you considered all the scheming that went into winning offices that didn't amount to much, except in name; but from another point of view campus politics were sound education. The deals behind the scenes, pitting one pressure group against another—that stuff was exciting, the kind of stuff you reported if you covered politics for a newspaper.

"Do I have a chance?" Jeremy insisted.

Creeper thought, I'm a fool. I've outgrown getting a kick out of posing as an amateur Machiavelli. I've been through the mill and I ought to be tired of it. But he was suddenly excited. Back in his freshman year the D.U.'s had knifed his chances for class presidency. Creeper thought he had forgiven that defeat, but now the thought of upsetting the combine planning to elect a D.U. to the senior class presidency became tremendously appealing.

"You've got a chance," Creeper said. "A good chance. But don't play your hand too soon. Wait until a week before the elections and catch 'em by surprise. Now I'll tell you how . . ."

Jeremy conceded at once that Creeper knew the game, and followed the managing editor's instructions without question. Two weeks before the elections the Barbarian Council met quietly and picked a slate of candidates. Then, in the final week, a round of smokers was held and the candidates announced. Jeremy toyed with the thought of assuring attendance at his smokers by bringing back the University physician, but there was a limit to even that patient man's good humor. As second choice the football coach drew remarkably well; he talked earnestly of schedules and of games that might have been won if this or that play had worked; the coach didn't discover what he was looking for—a blocking back to bolster his prospects for the coming season—but Jeremy found the votes he sought. When the election returns were tabulated, the Barbarians had swept the sophomore and senior elections and had come within a dozen votes of winning the junior class presidency. Jeremy, who had run for no office, strutted with elation; as the man behind the throne he prepared for newer and brighter worlds of conquest, and Creeper caught him one day coming from the library with a history of Tammany Hall under his arm.

"You'll get sick of it," Creeper predicted.

V

The time for naming a new *Targum* editor was less than a fortnight away. Jeremy had to face facts now; he had given more than a year to becoming a campus politician, and what had it availed him? The editor of *The Targum* was elected by a seven-man council, three members from the faculty and four undergraduate members (two Theta Zetes, two D.U.'s). Jeremy could count on Silvers's vote and through Silvers's influence upon the votes of the other faculty members; but unless he could swing some kind of political deal with the Thetes and the D.U.'s, he was going to lose the editorship by a vote of four to three. Jeremy's glumness grew deeper the longer he pondered his predicament; how was he going to make a deal with the Thetes and the D.U.'s when they had only to sit tight to assure their continued control over *The Targum?* They would be fools to concede him an inch—almost as big fools as he had been working day and night over the Barbarians, slighting his studies, serving as slop girl for every other nonfraternity man on the campus, and ending where he had begun: against a blank wall. The simple thought of how thoroughly he had been whipped by his own effort made him sick. It was during these hours of futility that Jeremy received news of Visch. Actually Muggsy received the news in a letter. Visch had been bounced from Dental School on the same old grounds that he hadn't the strength for making an extraction. Visch was staying on at Columbia and transferring to the curriculum in business administration, but his heart wasn't in it. Any time that Muggsy and Jeremy wanted to pull out for the South Seas they could count on him.

Muggsy folded the letter and Jeremy went on to *The Targum,* a Thursday night habit deep bred after more than two years. He was going to stick around until Creeper returned from *The Home News;* Creeper would tell him honestly whether he had even an outside chance of swinging one of those four undergraduate votes on Targum Council. When he reached College Avenue, he thought it strange that at this early hour a light should be blazing in Creeper's room.

Jack met him in the hallway. "It's Olanski. Hare's roommate. The State troopers found him over in the Sourland Mountains in a stolen car."

"Is he under arrest?"

"A little late for that," Jack said. "There was a .45 revolver beside him on the seat. He had blown his brains out."

Hearing their voices, Creeper came down the stairs.

"Come on over to Hare's room. Maybe he can tell us something about Olanski."

Jeremy still couldn't believe the news about Olanski as he and Creeper strode down the street toward Holy Hill. How little you really knew about what was going on inside somebody else's mind. You ignored some poor cuss because you thought he was quarrelsome or unsocial, and all the time the poor devil was struggling against the overpowering undertow of insanity.

"The tabloids will play this up for all it's worth," Creeper muttered worriedly. "Maybe they'll make it look like the college's fault—why didn't we know Olanski was off his nut? —but I don't think it was the college's fault. The guy would have gone over the edge anywhere."

"Some of us could have been kinder to the guy."

"Most of us don't give a hang about anything but ourselves. That's what makes Silvers, his selflessness. Maybe he could have touched Olanski if he had known him; maybe he could have given Olanski a faith outside himself to hang on to; but then, on the other hand, maybe nobody could."

"I should have told him about Olanski," Jeremy said dully.

Hare, his nerves coolly collected, met them at the door. "I can't tell you anything about Olanski that'll help. I lived with him but I never knew him."

"Was he a good student?" Creeper asked.

"He seemed to get by."

"Any prof he was close to?"

Hare shook his head. "He was too close to himself to have room for anybody else. You just thought of him as being queer and over moody. When he snapped out of it now and then, he talked rationally but always with an undertone of bitterness. He didn't trust anyone. He had no faith in anything."

Jeremy sat on the edge of Hare's desk, staring down at the floor. None of them could understand the Olanski case; it was above and beyond them. Olanski was merely a wretchedly unhappy figure from the dark streets of life who had wandered onto a college campus and so had touched their lives; now that he was gone they would try to forget him, for even in tragedy he had taught them nothing.

Creeper said, "It's a good thing for the college he didn't blow his brains out here."

Hare answered mechanically. "I guess he didn't think of it."

There wasn't anything more to say. They simply couldn't understand, even now. Walking back down Holy Hill, Jeremy kicked a stone and watched it bouncing ahead of him.

"We're fools," he said. "We worry over *Targum* elections, and an Olanski blows his brains out."

"We're sane, you mean. We find outlets. Olanski couldn't."

"Just the same it makes you think. It doesn't hurt to be kind to people. To believe a little in their goodness."

Creeper nodded. "And in their fairness—like Jack's swinging those four undergraduate votes so that you could be elected editor of *Targum* unanimously."

Jeremy stopped. "When did he do that, Creeper?"

"About a year ago—before you had dreamed up your Barbarians."

6

IN ABRAHAM'S BOSOM

I

If Jeremy's mind belonged to his classes and his heart to *The Targum,* his stomach belonged to Hertzog Hall. Set like a mother hen upon the crest of Holy Hill, this rambling, yellow stuccoed building was approached up a winding, cobbled driveway where the lights in the ancient lampposts gave the wayfarer the illusion of having stepped through time into the gas-jet era of tight-cuffed trousers and bowler hats. Hertzog was the pivot around which the life of the seminary revolved; here the theological students lived, attended classes and chapel services, and ate in their own dining hall. But there were always a number of rooms in Hertzog occupied by students from the college. These quarters might be a trifle bare, but they were clean and the rent was low; for a hundred dollars a year an undergraduate could obtain a study, a bedroom, and the cheerful companionship of mice running through the walls; in addition he could press his pants with the ministerial iron, hang his laundry upon the ministerial clothesline in the back of the building, and enjoy a certain degree of intimacy with men who were studying to become the spiritual leaders of his generation.

As an economy measure Jeremy came three times a day to eat with the seminarians. For $6.50 a week he found the fare plain but sustaining, with the exception of those days when salmon and liver were served, for the appearance of these un-imaginative dishes reminded him of all the cats and dogs he had raised as pets. But even though he subsisted largely on bread and milk and lemon custard during these meals, he continued to gain weight and to observe the manners and customs of those among his fellow men who professed to have heard the call.

Possibly the liver was to blame; this unsavory concoction aroused in Jeremy a nettlesome, ill-tempered streak. Muggsy ate the stuff—Muggsy ate everything. But brooding over his plate, Jeremy grumbled that seminarians, considered in-tellectually, were rather a seedy lot. Or on salmon days Jeremy argued that if a man with personality and a good mind wanted to pick a profession in which the competition was limited, the ministry was certainly it. But liver and sal-mon were not the only factors that turned Jeremy from be-liever into agnostic; there were other causes, inside and out of Hertzog.

A fat, moon-faced theologian with an unspellable Dutch name shortened to Berger first stirred Jeremy's doubt. Berger presided at the table where Jeremy, Muggsy, and four other interlopers from the college took their meals; Berger loved to eat, to laugh, and to be a good fellow; he suspected that the saying of grace before each meal was rather irksome to the college crowd and so, lowering his head, he would say in a mumbling rush:

"Good food, good meat, good God let's eat . . . Come on, fellows, let's shovel it down and be in time for seconds . . . Amen."

To Jeremy there wasn't anything funny about Berger's saying of grace; if Berger had gone into the ministry because he had heard the call, it must have been a mouse-like whisper, one that permitted him to compromise with the dignity of religion in form, in spirit, and in intent. No one in Jeremy's experience ever had made a joke of saying grace; no one ever had wanted to. Religion with a bedside manner—that was Berger, the flabby charlatan. Jeremy approached agnosticism for a reason that only the mind of a sophomore could grasp —his Puritanical principles had been outraged.

In Berger's room, in the dining hall, in the reading room on the second floor where the bewhiskered likenesses of the graduates of other generations appeared to glare down disapprovingly at the day-late issue of *The Christian Science Monitor* left there by one of the college crowd, Jeremy's contacts with the seminarians increased. Among student ministers as a group there was an attitude of shy trustfulness that Jeremy rather liked, although the naïveté of their humor and their lack of sophistication impressed him on some occasions as little short of simple-mindedness, and on other occasions as merely a professional pose. There were exceptions, perhaps fortunately and perhaps unfortunately, for such education as Jeremy absorbed from his association with the seminary came in large measure from the personalities who seemed to rise above the norm. Lyle Calvert, a sandy-haired, even-tempered New York state farmer turned clergyman, was one of those who exerted an influence upon him; Lyle's wholesome respect for God and religion served to offset the cynical compromise of Berger's antics.

One day when Jeremy and Lyle walked up the cobbled driveway to Hertzog, the seminarian asked, "Did you ever see a tree more beautiful than that old elm down there? Look at the spread of those branches, Jeremy, the strength in that tall old trunk. There's a sermon, a great sermon, in that tree!"

Jeremy watched a squirrel darting along one of the branches of the elm.

"This is the sermon, Jeremy: if a man can plant a seed and produce a tree like that, why can't he plant an idea and produce the same magnificent results? Why can't he, Jeremy? After all, the seed grows honestly, drawing its life from the resources of the soil, not to deplete those resources but actually to protect and replenish them. An idea can draw that strength from humanity if it is nurtured in the same honest spirit. That is the meaning of the line in the Bible, 'If ye had strength as a seed of mustard . . .'"

Jeremy looked again at the tree; the squirrel had disappeared; and a soft wind stirred the leaves so that they seemed to dance to a hidden music.

Lyle said, "Religion should mean a lot to you, Jeremy. A lot more to you than to the average person."

"Why?"

"An afflicted person needs the comfort of God. He needs the strength of a faith outside himself. He—"

Jeremy's tightening mouth stopped Lyle. The seminarian could not see where he had failed; a moment before he had sensed Jeremy's response to the sermon in the tree, but now there was a barrier between them. But Jeremy's disappointment was no less than Lyle's. He walked on, angered and rebellious. If Lyle's kind of religion had to distinguish between those who were physically handicapped and those who were not, Lyle could have it. This was bingo game religion, dressed up with traps and snares, and feeding on human weakness rather than on spiritual strength.

Jeremy went on into Hertzog thinking that between Berger and Lyle there existed only a question of degree in the extent to which they had begun to set him at odds against the Jeremy Baxter who only a year ago had stood with Iron Man and Muggsy in the battle of Darwinism. Sitting in judgment of the seminarians pleased Jeremy almost as much as sitting in judgment of his professors. It might have proved a rather monotonous, one-sided game if Berger and Lyle had been his sole adversaries. But Charlie the Bat remained.

The Bat lived in the center section, top floor, of Hertzog in three attic rooms known as Abraham's Bosom. No one who ate at Hertzog could avoid contact with the Bat, for he

was steward of the dining hall and insisted on prompt pay-
ment at the end of every week.

"Nothing doing," the Bat thundered when Muggsy
pleaded for a week's credit. "You'll take your $6.50 and spend
it on some girl. The girl'll get stout from overeating, which
won't do her any good, and we'll get skinny from lack of
finances in paying the butcher's bill. It's unchristian either
way you look at it, so fork over your $6.50, you heathen
chisler!"

Charlie the Bat had come to the seminary from a small
midwestern college that, to use his own description, was easy
to find—cross the Mississippi River, walk for six hundred
miles in a straight line toward Albuquerque, and you'd find
the college situated between a red barn and a corn field. The
Bat had been a ranch hand, a rodeo cowboy, a stevedore, a
seaman, and a Fuller Brush salesman before deciding to
prepare for the ministry. He possessed the native candor of
the midwesterner, the worldliness of the traveller to distant
climes, and the understanding of human nature that comes
from dashing off to be deloused the moment his ship reached
port. With the college crowd the Bat was a favorite, and that
was strange, for he didn't put himself out to spare their
feelings.

"So you think Berger is a fraud," the Bat said one night
when Jeremy loafed in the one over-stuffed chair that gave
Abraham's Bosom a note of homelikeness. "Well, maybe he
is, but listening to any of you punks from the college brand
anybody a fraud gives me a great big horse laugh!"

"Meaning what?"

"Precisely this. You think Berger has been untouched by
his college and seminary environments, but what can you
say for yourself? You're just touching the surface of education, glossing over the experience without acquiring any
depth. What do you know about real scholarship? Who ever

saw you in the library with your sleeves rolled up, digging for learning? You're just part of the norm, you little faker—you and Muggsy and nine tenths of your crowd."

"I didn't come to college to be a greasy grind," Jeremy said with dignity.

"Just greasy, eh?" The Bat chuckled happily. He was a tall, thickset fellow, a sort of gorilla-like creature with the surprising look of an ascetic in moments of repose. He was the most doggedly honest person that Jeremy ever had known, but he possessed as well a great capacity for kindness and tenderness.

"Kid," he said unexpectedly, "Berger's under your skin, isn't he? He's sort of undermining some of the props of your faith in the clergy?"

"I don't think he's sainted."

"Well hardly—not in the Dutch Reformed Church." The Bat smoked a pipe, but he found a pack of stale cigarettes in his desk, and offered one to Jeremy. "You're a product of your civilization and your generation, Jeremy."

"Aren't you?"

"Not so far as my faith in religion is concerned."

"Then you're a throwback to Neanderthal Man."

The Bat smiled; how these college kids liked to bandy about the catch phrases of erudition contemporary civilization loaded into their heads.

"I think this is what faith in God is," the Bat said. "It's a power that's born in each of us. We know it's there all the time, but somehow we find it hard to rely on its strength. Our lives become impeded with the getting and giving and what happens? The will to succeed in business, in a social sense, sets us at odds against ourselves. Little frustrations crop up a hundred times a day, and we become consumed with building defenses against them. Soon we are closed in within ourselves and away from our faith. And that's just the tragedy of man."

Jeremy was thinking that in another way the Bat was only telling him what Silvers had said on the day he had almost quit *The Targum*—about living in a valley or up on a hill. As long as the Bat was steward of the dining hall and he had to see him at least once every week, he really got his $6.50's worth at Hertzog.

II

Spring had come again. Jeremy sat in a rocker on the porch of Hertzog and looked down Holy Hill toward the college tennis courts. It was one of those fine spring days when everything about the campus seemed beautiful—Lyle's tall old elm, the freshly cut grass, the girls in their cotton print dresses walking up the path toward the library. Jeremy was only drowsily aware of the persons who passed him on the porch.

"What's going on?" he asked a lank, sober-faced seminarian who performed the function of welcoming committee.

"They're Oxford fellows."

"From Oxford, England?"

"No. From the college here. Haven't you heard of the Oxford Movement?"

Jeremy had—vaguely. It was a religious movement, he remembered; there were three seniors over in House Six, Hegeman, who convened every morning at six o'clock for prayer meeting. Some undergraduates thought that was funny. Jeremy didn't think it was funny; if he thought about it at all, it was simply that six o'clock was awfully early to get out of bed for anything, especially if you had been up till after midnight slaving on *The Targum*. Jeremy, settling down in the rocker, tried to surrender himself to the seductive lassitude of the drowsy spring afternoon. But his peacefulness was disturbed by the arrival of the Oxford Movement fellows; apparently Charlie the Bat was going to have a crowd up in Abraham's Bosom. Jeremy had to admit that the religious force was one of those things you couldn't rule out of the life of the college. The Oxford Movement followers represented only one crowd; the Y.M.C.A. had a group of its own, and you knew they existed for they came through the dorms every Christmas season soliciting funds to donate baskets to the needy families in New Brunswick; the Catholics had their Newman Society and the Jewish students their Menorah Society. Jeremy was tempted for a moment to climb the two long flights of stairs to Abraham's Bosom to see Charlie the Bat in action, but in the end the physical labor involved discouraged him. That was one pleasing aspect about labelling yourself an agnostic; if you felt lazy where religion was concerned, you could always hide your indolence behind the cloak of an intellectual principle.

So far Jeremy would only admit that he was an agnostic— that he didn't know what to believe. He wasn't like Toady Reed over in House One, Hegeman, who called himself an atheist. The funny part of it was, Toady went to church every Sunday, but he rarely went to the same church twice in succession; one Sunday he would be a Presbyterian, the next a Catholic, the next a Christian Scientist, and so on down the list of all the denominations until about the thirteenth or fourteenth week of every term, when Toady would declare a bit wickedly that he felt Brigham Young-ish and became a Mormon. Toady spent the remainder of the week ridiculing the service he had attended, and he felt that he was an extremely fair-minded person because he ridiculed them all. Toady's other hobby was tracing the respectable derivations of the four-letter words which are now considered unprintable except in the modern American novel; on either subject, religion or barroom philology, Toady could keep you up half the night listening to him, except that after one session Toady seemed a terrible bore.

Toady was the rascal who had brought one of Lizzie Whitman's classes to the brink of riot. Now that he recalled his part in the affair, Jeremy could still feel shamefaced at his brashness. The incident had taught him many things—how strongly a man can come to depend upon his faith; how cruelly thoughtless and rude youth can be. Lizzie was a good teacher in Jeremy's estimation; after all, he was head of the Department of English and his position stood for something. But not in Toady's eyes; he looked upon Lizzie as a sentimental old man who had grown tyrannical in his dogmatism. Perhaps the eruption would not have been half so violent if it had not come so unexpectedly. Lizzie liked to read poetry in his classes, and his course in masterpieces of literature gave him many opportunities to indulge this fondness. He read well, a man with a rich, deep voice who expressed himself with great dignity of feeling. Robert Browning's "Rabbi Ben Ezra" was the subject of class discussion that day, and Lizzie read the opening stanza:

> "Grow old along with me!
> The best is yet to be,
> The last of life, for which the first was made:
> Our times are in His hand
> Who saith, 'A whole I planned,
> Youth shows but half; trust God; see all, nor
> be afraid!' "

Lizzie put down his book. He had read the passage, obviously deeply stirred; he was that sort of man who could not conceal his emotion. "Gentlemen," he said, "I ask you, could there be a more beautiful philosophy for facing life?"

A voice in the last row—Toady's voice—replied curtly, "Sounds like sour grapes to me!"

Lizzie's head snapped back as though he had been slapped. "How dare you say that!"

"It's no philosophy of life at all," Toady insisted, "but a defeated man's apology to himself. It's the tawdry theological argument that would comfort every weakling. 'Grow old along with me, the best is yet to be . . .' What right has Browning to be so smug about himself, or to think that God gives a hoot whether or not he starves to death?"

"I can assure you, Mr. Reed, that Mr. Browning did not starve to death."

"Well, better he had then, Mr. Whitman, handing out that sop for a philosophy. Religion is based on that doctrine of complacency. Accept whatever you are and be happy in God. It's a philosophy of admitted weakness."

"I feel no shame in acknowledging a human frailty before God," Lizzie said tartly. In the tilt of Lizzie's chin there was a hint of pugnacity, giving credence to the story that as an undergraduate at Yale Lizzie had been an intercollegiate boxing champion.

The debate grew general and Toady revelled in what he had started. Jeremy supported Toady; young men were forever being told by their elders to be satisfied with what they had and what they were merely because their elders had lost hope of ever being any better off and so had to be satisfied. The doctrine of original sin was dragged into the argument by another student, who said he denied that he had been conceived in sin and would support no religion that insulted his intelligence. Muggsy swerved the argument away from religion into history. When did a civilization flourish except in its youth? The decline of the Roman and Greek civilizations were good examples. As young civilizations they had thrived, for there had been idealism to support them; but with age there had been only an accumulation of wickedness, an acceptance of the evil influence of corruption, the decadence of a waning spirit.

"You think Mr. Browning's spirit is waning in those beautiful lines?" Lizzie asked.

"Waning—and waned," Toady interrupted. "His poem is a fake, built upon a false premise. Every catchpenny prophet since the dawn of speech has won an audience by the same trick of saying 'Lose your guilt in me.' "

Lizzie made no attempt to answer Toady directly. His voice was choked; his face flushed; his eyes unashamedly filled with tears. His whole concept of life was expressed in those lines by Browning.

"You disappoint me, gentlemen. You disappoint me deeply. The class is dismissed."

Toady strode from the room, triumphant. But Jeremy was aghast at how deeply Dr. Whitman had been shaken by the attack upon his principles. It had been wrong. All undergraduates talked loosely among themselves, but they needed to draw a line. Youthfulness by itself gave no warrant to be vicious in supporting its prejudices. And what more had they been? Lizzie deserved the right to judge his own destiny as good or bad.

Sitting on the porch of Hertzog, Jeremy remembered Lizzie's eyes and wished he hadn't taken part in the discussion. He had been led astray by Toady, and Toady's beliefs weren't his beliefs. Between Toady and the Oxford Movement crowd he was somewhere in the middle—not too much believer, not too much disbeliever. He was willing to concede that his apathy toward religion was partially a matter of laziness and convenience, but not altogether so. He hadn't been much of a church-goer before coming to college, and the habit of observing religious ritual simply wasn't deep bred in him as it was in Iron Man or in Muggsy. Perhaps underneath he really believed—and wanted to believe.

He knew what Charlie the Bat would say—Jeremy didn't know enough not to believe. The only church history he had studied were the fragments that had been part of the course in contemporary civilization; there was a course in Bible and ethics, but it was an elective and in his first two years he hadn't found time for it. What he knew about religion was hit or miss, picked up from Muggsy and Toady and the semi-narians. Muggsy had started him reading the Bible, but he had never finished it; he had stumbled on Papini's *Life of Christ,* and that had told him just about everything without struggling over who begat whom. Papini's story of Christ was exciting, beautiful reading; he had been enthralled by every page and had carried the book to classes with him. But Mencken's *Treatise on the Gods* had fallen into his hands about that time, and he had gone through it in two nights, troubled, uncertain. There had been an almost sadistic joy in the reasonableness with which Mencken had reduced all faith to the lunatic fringe of mythology; you finished with Mencken and there seemed no prophet remaining except Mencken himself, and who wanted a prophet who posed for his picture wearing a pair of red suspenders? Muggsy had invested a dime with the Swedenborg Foundation and had received an arm full of tracts, but Jeremy hadn't been able to hold his interest through more than a page or two. Once you began reading the pros and cons of religion, there were mountains of books on both sides, but you ended where you began until all you could think of were those lines by Auden—

> *And every man in every generation,*
> *Tossing in his dilemma on his bed,*
> *Cries to the shadows of the noble dead.*

Colonel Axton, the college chaplain, would discuss religion with you, but the old colonel reduced the whole matter to an Army man's level—faith was part of regulations. Burns in C.C. tried to be fair with church history, but underneath you suspected the tinge of an anticleric. Somehow church history and cynicism made poor bedfellows. In the end there was only the debate within yourself, and the conviction that it was easier not to worry about the subject at all. Perhaps it came down to a simple solution, anyhow. If God could become completely comprehensible to a man, He would no longer be God. Miracles were unexplainable—that fact made them miracles. Beyond death and time and space . . . no one could know. What Charlie the Bat had said that night about faith in God made sense; the Bat made you feel faith was something you should hang onto, and keep telling yourself you had.

Jeremy brushed away a fly that buzzed by his nose. He wondered what Berger did on a fine day like this. Berger tried so hard to be part of the crowd, congenial and tolerant —it was a strange trait to condemn him for. And Lyle tried simply to be good, so good that sooner or later you felt like a punk by comparison—because you had listened to an off-color story where Lyle wouldn't, because you swore or drank a glass of beer or turned around to look twice at a girl. Berger set no example and Lyle too much example. And yet even Berger had moments of thoughtfulness that made him seem worthy of his calling. Jeremy had seen him go out in the rain to offer a poor old lady his umbrella. Somehow Jeremy was mixed up when he tried to condemn the seminarians for their religion, or religion for the seminarians. The answer was always coming back to himself; as Charlie the Bat said, he was lost in the maze of his own defense mechanisms; it made him tired to think about the problem any longer. The spring air was sweet in his lungs. The soft breeze came tenderly to caress his face. What a week end it promised to be for going off on a hike! But Jeremy pushed the thought aside, reluctantly and then rebelliously; he had already used his quota of Sunday chapel cuts.

III

It rained on Sunday, but Jeremy never lacked for a reason to resent that he had to go to chapel. His disposition wasn't improved by the fact that his razor was dull; scratched and bleeding, he went off to the eleven o'clock services, grimly telling himself that the rebellion against compulsory Sunday chapel was more widespread than the college authorities suspected, and wondering with an irked contempt what bald-headed Berger they would dig up to occupy the pulpit this morning.

But when some minutes later Jeremy sat in the quiet old chapel, much of his irritation had faded. The rain stopped and the sun creeping through the opened windows was warm and cheerful as it fell in bright banners upon the walls and wooden pews. The soft music of the organ, the flowers banked around the altar, the figure of Christ in the stained glass window above the chancel possessed a feeling of repose and of elevation; here hung the visages of graduates of the college who had brought honor to her name since pre-Revolutionary times; the portrait of Simeon DeWitt, class of 1776, who had been geographer to General Washington's army; of William A. Newell, class of 1836, onetime governor of New Jersey and later governor of the State of Washington; of Garret A. Hobart, class of 1863, vice-president of the United States. Jeremy experienced a sense of pride as he studied the faces that looked back at him from the silent walls; some of the names he recognized and others he did not, but he knew that all of these scores of graduates had in their generation brought greatness to the college and to the nation. Opening his chapel program Jeremy saw that the speaker was a rabbi of national reputation, that the flowers on the altar had been donated by the members of Zeta Psi fraternity in memory of a member of the chapter who had died four years before.

Jeremy sat back against the hard pew and thought of all the times he had been in chapel: on Sunday mornings like this, on Tuesdays at noon when his whole class met to hear announcements, at Christmas for the Yuletide music, on the opening day of freshman week. He liked the old place; part of him was rooted here. The organ music stopped, and Jeremy bent forward and leaned his head against his arms for the opening prayer. Charlie the Bat prayed every noon; Jeremy knew, because he had walked into Abraham's Bosom one day when the Bat was kneeling by his bed.

"Pray with me," the Bat had said.

Embarrassed, Jeremy had knelt beside the Bat. They had prayed in silence—Jeremy asking God mostly to forgive him for feeling like such a fool and a hypocrite. But Charlie the Bat had seemed to understand.

"It takes practice," he had said. "God knows that you're an amateur."

Good old Bat, Jeremy thought. The Bat made reverence beautiful and comfortable. He made it real and intelligent. No slobbering about leaning on God in your physical infirmities. Jeremy caught himself and joined with the congregation: "Our Father who art in heaven . . ."

The organ resumed playing, the choir stood up, and Jeremy sank back once more in his pew seat to listen. The voices were young, strong, firm voices; Jeremy felt his spirits lifted with the music. But principally he was conscious of a feeling of peace; he closed his eyes and thought: "Here if I try the Bat and I are one in spirit." When he opened his eyes once more he saw Lizzie Whitman across the aisle. The man smiled and Jeremy thought now: " 'Grow old along with me, the best is yet to be. . . .' " Jeremy was ashamed at the callousness of his own youth, remembering how he had helped to upset Lizzie that day.

The sermon began and Jeremy found his interest carried along by the rabbi who spoke simply of the faith that dwelled in every man's heart, Jew and gentile, Negro and white. Faith, he said, was the wisdom of goodness. Jeremy liked the the thought. He thought back, Sunday after Sunday, about the men who had supplied the pulpit in the college chapel. Each had spoken in a homely language, and yet they had each given him a sense of well-being. Why? Had it been himself to whom he had really listened—as his heart could say now, here is faith and therefore here is goodness also? Jeremy wondered. Chapel had forced him to sit before some of the really great spiritual leaders of his age—men from every denomination, men of intellectual maturity who had dignified both the academic gowns they wore and the figure of Christ in the the stained glass window above the chancel. Some day Charlie the Bat would preach in a college chapel.

The services ended. Jeremy moved into the crowded aisle, and a classmate pushed against his shoulder.

"That's over for another week," the other boy said.

Jeremy nodded, but his heart wasn't in the nod. He wanted to cling to the illusion of peace that had come upon him. Why couldn't reverence be more popular? Why did he have to feel stiff within himself when the Bat asked him to kneel in prayer? What was this thing in him that made him nod and snicker and rebel at chapel because someone else did?

He went on into the warm sunlight, hungry, setting his course in brisk strides toward Hertzog. He was still conscious, however, that he struggled to grasp a truth. Once he could rise above kidding himself, he could become his own most rewarding textbook. He could grumble about a few seminarians like Berger and Lyle, but he could comprehend that religion was safe under the guardianship of seminarians like the Bat; he could pose as an agnostic, but he could admit that there was no philosophical depth to his rebellion, and that he believed faith was a stronger challenge than lack of faith; he could condemn compulsory chapel, but he could know that he objected to the effort of going, not to what he heard preached. For a time—for months and even years perhaps— he could be unaware of this awakening within himself; but Silvers and the dean of men and Charlie the Bat could not, for unless they could measure such changes they each belonged in other callings.

IV

At the end of Jeremy's sophomore year the university acquired a new president. Robert C. Clothier came to Rutgers with a brand it was rather difficult for the undergraduates to forgive—he was a graduate of Princeton—but the man's happy frankness in confessing that he not only wanted to see the Rutgers football team play Princeton but to leave the Princeton Tiger with its tail tied to the goal posts served rather well in obscuring his own shady undergraduate background. Within a week after Jeremy had become editor of *The Targum,* he received an invitation from the president to come to his office to discuss college matters of "mutual concern."

"You know what that means," Muggsy taunted. "He suspects that you're an infidel and a radical. Very likely he doesn't like the way you wear your old school tie."

Jeremy scowled. "Who's Clothier? He's only the president."

"That's a point."

"The students own *The Targum.* I'll go see Clothier if I can work it in my schedule."

Rather fortuitously, Jeremy succeeded in arranging his schedule to be at Clothier's office at two o'clock the following Tuesday afternoon—the time suggested in the president's letter.

President Clothier received Jeremy with respectfulness for the position he held as editor. Since in a sense they were both just starting out on their jobs, Clothier explained that he hoped they could help each other. That part of a university president's success depended on the respect and affection he won from the undergraduates scarcely occurred to Jeremy; he was captivated by the man's forthrightness and friendliness; at no time during the ivy years was Jeremy to know a feeling of greater importance than now as he freely and gladly gave the president advice on what was right and wrong with the college.

Clothier listened patiently. "How about Sunday chapel? How do you think we should feel about that?"

"Well, now there, sir," Jeremy began, and then stopped. There had been editorials in *Targum* in years past deriding compulsory chapel, but did he believe them? As an editor he was responsible for molding campus opinion. But the question went deeper—deeper even than saying the right thing to curry favor. The real question was in him, in what he knew as truth.

"Couldn't you say it this way, Jeremy? The education of a man is like a three-legged stool. We cultivate his mind and that's one leg. Another leg is developing a sound body, through athletics and military training and habits of clean living. But there's still a third part to the man—his spiritual self—and can we afford to overlook that?"

Jeremy shook his head. A man lived a good part of the day within himself; it was there his education had to reach him if it were to have complete meaning. At the door he shook Clothier's hand and went away glad that there was warmth in the man's clasp.

So he had come to it at last, Jeremy thought. He had completed the cycle from believer to agnostic to believer again. He felt just a bit uneasy. Or had he curried favor—simply played the game you had to play once in awhile to get ahead? Some profs marked easier if you laughed at their lousy jokes. Some profs opened up with a little flattery. You knew it and so you laughed or leg-pulled, but underneath you felt dishonest. It was a game you played, but you had to watch out for it. Within yourself.

But he knew Clothier was right. The force of religion was deep—as Charlie the Bat said, your faith was there, born in you, part of the flesh and bone, and you could run away from it if you liked but you were only running down a long, lonely road that seemed to lead further and further into the obscure forests of doubt and distrust and inward rebellion. A Berger didn't matter. Or a Lyle Calvert. Or some humorless, simple-hearted seminarian who made you want to open his skull to see if there was anything more inside than a couple of mice out of the walls of Hertzog. Charlie the Bat was real. And Prexy. And those portraits on the walls of chapel.

He saw her as she came slowly down College Avenue. She was a little old lady, her shoulders bent, her gait shuffling and hesitant. She wore the black of mourning, and the shawl over her head gave emphasis to her weathered, wrinkled skin. Her lips had the parched look that comes with age, her eyes the far away look that hard work and hard suffering are likely to put into an old person's eyes. In her hand she clutched a crucifix, but the touch of her fingers appeared gentle, the smile on her lips soft and alive and enduring.

Jeremy passed her and then looked back. A little old lady dressed in black. But she was real, too.

The religious force existed. He knew; he had eyes that could see. And it meant something to admit that even now, for this had been a liver day at Hertzog Hall.

7

SPOOK'S HOLE

I

Jeremy first beheld Spook's Hole on a sultry Indian Summer day in September of his junior year.

His mother said, "I hate to think of it, Jeremy. After your two years in Hegeman it hurts me to have you living in a place like this."

Jeremy glanced at the three-story, frame rooming house on Bartlett Street. The building possessed the appearance of drabness which comes to houses that have outlived their prime and can claim no mark of distinction to soften the gauntness of their declining years.

"Now, Mom," Jeremy said, bolstering his own spirits, "it's a roof over my head and it's lots cheaper than the rent in Hegeman."

Mrs. Baxter followed her son along the uneven flagstone walk that led to a porch badly in need of paint. She watched the rather stiff, determined jerkiness that had come into Jeremy's stride and smiled. Once years ago when she had seen him walking off to a baseball game with his father she had noticed this peculiarity in his gait.

Mrs. Bridewell, who ran the rooming house on Bartlett Street, greeted them from her chair in the front sitting room. A goiter had deformed her throat and had given her head a shrunken, ill-proportioned appearance in contrast to her large-boned body; against the dingy wallpaper her presence in the room possessed a quality of unreality, as though a moment before she had been a figure in the faded covering on the walls and a moment hence might dissolve back into the paper; she sat with a cane between her legs and even in repose seemed to be leaning on it for support.

"I have Jeremy's room all ready for him on the third floor," the landlady said. "That will be three dollars a week —in advance."

Jeremy's mother said nothing, but she found it an effort not to. Three dollars a week each from Jeremy and his roommate for an attic room came to approximately twenty-six dollars a month. Mrs. Baxter reflected that paralysis may have incapacitated Mrs. Bridewell's legs, but the affliction certainly had not handicapped her business acumen.

"You can go right up," Mrs. Bridewell said more cheerfully, tucking into her apron pocket the three one dollar bills Jeremy handed her, "but be careful when you reach the turn in the stairs to the third floor. I wouldn't want you bumping your heads since I haven't any insurance covering such accidents."

Jeremy's mother no longer cared if the vexation did show in her eyes; there was plenty she could say, but most of all she wanted to fight back the tears that threatened to betray her ruffled pride.

"Careful," Jeremy chuckled when they reached the slanting beam of the roof that fell over the turn in the stairs. He ducked his own head and saw the discarded furniture, the piles of newspapers and *Saturday Evening Posts* that filled the unfinished attic beyond.

"It's a firetrap," Mrs. Baxter said unhappily.

Jeremy waited for his mother to negotiate the bend in the stairs and admitted that the slanting beam was hard on a stout person. But leaning against a battered chest of drawers whose casterless legs tipped under his weight, he spoke with a touch of impatience. "Look, Mom, money's tight with us. I can make out here—it's a place to sleep—and it'll save a lot. It's this or no college and so this is fine!"

The woman had known that this moment must come some day, but she had never expected to meet it in this miserable attic on the edge of a university campus. One day her boy had gone off to a baseball game with his father and she had lost her baby. On another day the boy had refused her well-intended counsel and had stomped away to his own room, touchy and moody and inwardly impeded; and she had recognized the first dreadful symptoms of adolescence. But now the boy accepted adversity without any thought of self-pity, but simply as a mean justified by the end it served; and he seemed grown up, reliant, a man. She was proud of him.

The room itself was really much nicer than she had expected. Of course a double bed instead of two single beds was not at all to her liking. But there were two study tables, two comfortable lounge chairs, a good overhead light, convenient floor plugs, and a pair of screened windows that looked out through the trees upon a pleasant glimpse of the campus.

"Cozy and good enough," Jeremy declared.

"It's hot," his mother said. "Very likely it'll be cold in winter."

"Then we'll throw an extra blanket on the bed and study there."

Silently the woman thanked her son for his steadfastness. She knew that she was going to cry driving home alone, but not now. He had grown so much. She saw that fact so clearly, and she felt that somehow the college had helped him. She couldn't realize entirely how his candor and honesty in accepting himself had been influenced by many factors, among them his associations with Creeper and Charlie the Bat; but she could recognize that his habit of brushing back an unruly lock of hair was a habit he shared with Earl Reed Silvers, for she had noticed the same trait in both of them when she had come down to Parents Day services in the chapel one Sunday last May.

"Do be careful," Mrs. Baxter pleaded. "If you came up those stairs heedlessly—and you know how you always run up stairs—you might strike your head and have a brain concussion."

"Don't worry, Mom, I'll be careful."

"Well, I surely hope you will." Mrs. Baxter, standing in the outer attic, spied a copy of *The Saturday Evening Post* featuring a Mister Glencannon story she hadn't read. "I'll take that home with me," she said, her mouth tight with determination as she stuffed the magazine into an empty brown bag. The satisfaction she took in filching the magazine from Mrs. Bridewell was unmistakable.

Jeremy chided her about it as he waited for her to start the car.

"It doesn't bother my conscience, Jeremy. Not a bit. You're being overcharged by that woman. Shamefully."

When the car turned the corner into College Avenue, Jeremy turned back to the porch. Another student had come out of Mrs. Bridewell's, and Jeremy recognized him as a classmate called Whiskers, because he rarely shaved. In two years of college Jeremy had not spoken more than a dozen words to Whiskers, whom he had privately despised as a grind, but now his spirits lifted at the sight of a familiar face.

"Rather warm, isn't it?"

"Hadn't noticed."

"Going to be tough at football practice, this hot spell."

"Let the fools sweat."

Whiskers, with his pimply nose rather up in the air, charged down the steps without another word. There were two library books under his arm. Jeremy shuddered. If Whiskers was typical of Mrs. Bridewell's other roomers, the place was going to be cozy.

Back in his room, Jeremy stretched out on the bed and surveyed his new college home. He liked it, he guessed; it was almost too hot to like anything. He couldn't keep his thoughts from drifting back to the memory of Hegeman—to the freshman year when he had shared the companionship of Muggsy and Visch and Iron Man and the Haldeman-Julius sage, to the sophomore year when Muggsy and he had occupied rooms across the hall. He didn't relish the idea of sleeping in the double bed or of sharing the one clothes closet. But mostly he was lonesome—for Hegeman, for Muggsy. He hoped that Duncan Faust, his roommate, would arrive that evening. But Duncan didn't.

Jeremy slept fretfully, troubled by the heat and by his loneliness. Toward midnight he was awakened by a noise outside his window. Across the street in a house not unlike Mrs. Bridewell's residence lived the members of Omicron Alpha Tau. Unable to sleep in the heat, the brothers of O.A.T., clad only in their pajamas, had taken to parading up and down the porch steps while they sang lustily:

> *My father sent me to old Rutgers*
> *And resolved that I should be a man. . . .*

Sitting half naked by the window, Jeremy watched the pajama brigade and thought that even from the breathless heights of Mrs. Bridewell's attic it was good, mighty good, to be back.

II

Duncan Faust arrived next morning, and Jeremy forgot his nostalgia for Hegeman. Gaunt, six-feet-two, with features almost Lincolnesque in their sharpness, Duncan fitted easily into the life at Mrs. Bridewell's, for he was a third-year resident there. Duncan was Mrs. Bridewell's favorite among the six students from the university who shared her dwelling. Duncan never complained if he waited half an hour to get into the single bathroom while Mrs. Bridewell's daughter

Kathie fussed with her hair; Duncan knew that the moment he appeared in the kitchen intending to press his trousers with the Bridewell iron the mistress of the house would remember some item she had forgotten to order from the store and Duncan would run the errand, not minding the fact that he was victimized every time. Apparently nothing ever ruffled Duncan's disposition, least of all the knowledge that his grades were without distinction or that he never won at penny ante during those early morning sessions in Patsy DiOrio's room when, as the play grew heated, Mrs. Bridewell pounded on the floor with her cane and Kathie, creeping up the stairs, thrust her head through the door to plead, "Keep shouting, fellows. The old woman will skin me alive if she hears me still up at quarter to two!"

Jeremy liked Kathie; she had a round, pert little face and a style for wearing clothes; and she possessed good sense, too, for she was friendly with all six student-roomers without inviting the least misunderstanding on their part.

"I'll tell you why," Duncan said maliciously. "A couple of years ago there was a junior lived here named Bus Johnson. Kathie let him kiss her, but Bus had trench mouth and Kathie got it, and now she acts as though everybody at Rutgers had trench mouth!"

Jeremy heard the story with disappointment; Kathie with curlers in her hair might make him notice the lines that already were creeping into her face, but the other night when Kathie had worn that gray sweater and her hair had been all fluffed up, he had wondered if what Patsy DiOrio was always talking about would be fun.

"Kathie?" Duncan laughed.

But Jeremy wanted badly to go with a girl. Why not Kathie? And yet he was no fool. The atmosphere of Mrs. Bridewell's breathed the warning that if you wanted to get along, the traditions of the household had better be respected—in regard to Kathie especially. He'd be happier if he were more like Whiskers, or if he didn't listen to Patsy's sexy talk. He found a simple way of getting Mrs. Bridewell's daughter out of his mind. Whenever he thought of Kathie he thought of hair curlers. This self-discipline worked more effectively than the saltpeter Duncan declared the college authorities put into the cafeteria food. When Duncan discoursed on this subject, Jeremy always conjured up in his mind a picture of no less a person than the president of the university at work in the cafeteria kitchen—one pinch for freshmen, two for sophomores, three for juniors and seniors. Talking seriously about sex meant you were thinking about it, but laughing at sex was laughing at yourself in a sense, and it was easier to keep your balance.

"Kathie, you know," Duncan said one day, "is thirty-four."

At twenty-one Jeremy was appalled to think how aged Kathie actually was.

The presence of Kathie—in hair curlers or a sweater—was only one evidence that Mrs. Bridewell's simply was not Hegeman; life on Bartlett Street claimed irritating little restrictions and inconveniences unknown during Jeremy's two carefree years in the dormitory; he chafed at climbing the stairs to Spook's Hole, at Whiskers's gruffness and unfriendliness, at the discovery of wads of dust behind the radiator. When Mrs. Bridewell, aggravated by her monthly bills, decreed that since a radio used extra electricity each radio in the room should incur a charge of twenty-five cents weekly, Jeremy was ready to lead a rebellion.

But easy-going Duncan said, "Aw, pay it."

"Or the old lady can ask you to get out," Patsy suggested.

Jeremy took his defeat badly. Money threatened to remain tight at home for a long while; he had to stay on at Spook's Hole. But he didn't have to like it or to feel respectful toward the others who shared Mrs. Bridewell's lodgings with him. That grind Whiskers was intolerable, Duncan had no backbone, and Patsy's dirty talk grew boresome. George Prentiss and Rudy Clarke, who occupied the front room on the second floor, were a pair of senior engineers who owned everything in common—textbooks, slide rule, tuxedo, and, Jeremy suspected, tooth brush. They were a humorless pair, untutored in any subject not directly connected with engineering, and prim and economical in conversation. Jeremy went for days without being aware that either of them existed.

"You'd think you'd at least meet them waiting to get into the johnny," he complained to Duncan.

"They're not majoring in *sanitary* engineering."

Jeremy laughed; Duncan was all right; he had more spark than the others. Of course for aggressiveness no one at Bridewell's outclassed Whiskers. He talked the old lady into permitting him to convert the outer attic into a studio, and without paying a nickel extra. That fact annoyed Jeremy most.

Midway through October the weather suddenly turned crisp and cool, and Jeremy's good spirits revived. Coming back to Mrs. Bridewell's late one afternoon, Jeremy scuffled happily through the dry leaves and decided that life was not so bad after all. Kathie was at home ironing in the kitchen, her hair tight with curlers, but with rare charity Jeremy forgave even that affront to his sensibilities. When he started up the stairs to the third floor, a light burning in the outer attic informed him that Whiskers was laboring in his "studio," but the buoyancy of the autumn day still lingered and even the intrusion of Whiskers's presence seemed forgivable.

In a sweat shirt and a pair of ragged trousers, Whiskers worked at an easel propped against the casterless chest of drawers. Daubs of paint were on his hands and face and in his hair, and there were streaks of it upon his shirt where Whiskers, preoccupied with his painting, had wiped his hands absent-mindedly. Whiskers's powers of concentration were remarkable; not by so much as a tilt of his head did he give any indication of awareness that someone had come into the attic. Jeremy's glance swept past Whiskers to the canvas on which the student artist was working with his dark eyes fiercely a-squint; Jeremy was forced to admit that the scene Whiskers was painting was really good—Queen's Campus on a fall evening with the leafless trees appearing gaunt and naked.

"I like that!"

Whiskers grunted.

"You know, it's good—realistic."

"Thank you."

"Must have taken a lot of work."

"Not enough."

"Don't you like your own painting?"

"I think it's lousy!"

Jeremy shook his head. He was no art critic, but that painting looked good. "What's wrong with it?"

Whiskers laid down his brush and turned around. His bushy hair already had begun to recede from his forehead, and his eyes, almost jet black, luminous and intelligent, seemed overlarge against the uncertain light from the single bulb. "Look," he said, "we don't talk the same language."

"Why not?"

"Because we don't. You like the painting, and maybe you should. That painting's like you and your crowd. All surface. All facility, if you can understand an art term. No depth, not enough sweat, not a shred of conscientious technique. It's too easy, too frothy, too lacking in meaning. Just another picture, as you'll go out of here some day just another guy holding a hunk of paper called an A.B. degree."

Jeremy could feel his temper rising. "Do I have to be a stinking grind to tell a good painting from a bad one?"

Whiskers laughed. "The way you use that word 'grind'— as though you were spitting out venom. If a chap wants to make an honest effort to get something out of his books, if he's willing to dig for an education, if he thinks sex isn't the only interesting subject in the world, if he wants to learn honest craftsmanship instead of just getting by in the same old rut of mediocrity like your friends, then he's something distasteful, eh?"

"I didn't say that."

"No, and you didn't think it. It's not being facile to think that way about yourself. It's not very pleasant. After all, you can get by in college as a '3' student, and that's only 70 per cent. Only a borderline nitwit needs to flunk out."

"You feel pretty superior, don't you?"

"To your crowd? Why not?"

Jeremy was tired of being insulted; his nerves were becoming jumpy, and that made him angry also. Then Whiskers had painted a lousy painting and he and Duncan and all his friends were a crowd of cheap four-flushers. Let it go at that. He slammed the door to his room.

But the incident stayed with him. Probably Whiskers was right about the painting. The admission unsettled him. It had never occurred to him that a man might be able to do something too easily—like Whiskers painting Queen's Campus or Silvers writing another book for kids.

Jeremy was deeply, unidentifiably troubled.

Duncan merely thought that what Whiskers had said was funny, but for once Jeremy found it difficult to be so lighthearted. He wouldn't be living in Spook's Hole if his reserve funds hadn't been mostly gone and if money at home hadn't been scarce. His tuition wouldn't have been paid if pop hadn't cashed in his insurance policy. The sacrifice behind his being in college was something he felt acutely; it hurt to lose at a penny ante game in Patsy DiOrio's room or to pay Mrs. Bridewell the extra quarter every week for the privilege of turning on the radio. He had to think of those things.

There had to be a better solution, and Jeremy, living with the problem day and night, decided at the end of another week that he had found it. Working one's way through college had become enshrined with not a little nobility, and Jeremy intended having a fling at it. The university operated an Office of Personnel and Placement whose chief function was finding employment for students financially hard-pressed; the jobs offered through this office in any one academic year catered to a wide variety of talents—part-time typists, furnace tenders, window washers, house cleaners, store clerks, night watchmen, guardians for an evening of the children of one of the professors, chauffers, automobile mechanics, program salesmen at football games, tutors, operators of the hat checking concessions at concerts and dances, assistants in the library, gardeners, and, in one instance, companion to a ninety-year-old gentleman whose principal interest in life revolved around hiring someone whom he could trounce at cribbage. To Jeremy there seemed to be neither permanency nor future in these types of employment; at best it was working for chicken feed and at worst it was stifling a spirit of free enterprise.

He discussed the subject with Duncan. "Dordy Heyd has a good racket delivering morning newspapers around the campus. They say Dordy makes as much as fifteen bucks a week, and look at all the publicity Silvers got him—the varsity halfback who conditions himself with an early morning paper route."

"We're not halfbacks," Duncan said, "and I'm not getting up at five-thirty every morning!"

"Well, there's Sam Bevin making out mighty well with his photography studio in that hole-in-the-wall on Easton Avenue. They say that on a prom week end when all the guys want to be mugged with their girls Sam cleans up. And there's Tom Craig with his tutoring lessons in freshman math; Tom's gotten as high as two bucks an hour. If we only had some hobby to ride like Sam or Tom it'd be easy."

"We haven't," Duncan said, not the least disheartened.

Jeremy rolled a pillow under his head and gazed up at the ceiling. The blue paint was streaked and faded—another example, he supposed, of how too much facility produced shoddy craftsmanship. "And then there's Aaron," he said after a moment. "There's an idea!"

Duncan's meditation was always labored. Everyone on the campus knew Aaron—good-natured, loose-kneed, gold-toothed Aaron who was present wherever a crowd gathered, lugging a white box supported by a strap slung over his shoulder. Aaron sold popsicles and brick ice cream in hot weather, hot dogs and coffee when frosts and snow crept over the campus. Aaron made a mint of money.

"But Aaron's overlooked the best bet of all," Jeremy said. "When's a fellow hungriest? At about ten in the evening when he's finished studying or has resigned himself to the fact that he doesn't intend to study, anyhow. A couple of enterprising guys who circulated through the dorms and fraternities at about that time offering sandwiches, candy bars, apples, and brick ice cream for sale really ought to strike it rich!"

Duncan nodded, only lukewarm in his conviction, but the nod committed him. Never good at figures, Jeremy toiled for an hour before he announced the minimum investment on which they could launch their sandwich route—two dollars for a pair of fiber marketing baskets, a dollar and a half for cold cuts and cheese, twenty cents for two loaves of bread, twenty cents for half a pound of butter, a dime for a jar of mustard, thirty cents for three rolls of wax paper, a dollar and twenty cents for three quarts of brick ice cream (Louie would throw in the dry ice for nothing), and ninety-five cents for a basket of apples; a total of $8.45. Still uncertain concerning the whole idea, Duncan contributed $4.20 as his share in the business and tossed Jeremy for the extra nickel. Jeremy lost.

The sandwiches were made on top of the casterless chest of drawers in the outer attic. Duncan buttered one slice of bread and smeared mustard on the other while Jeremy doled out with miserly carefulness one slice of boiled ham and one slice of cheese for each sandwich. Retail price: fifteen cents with no reduction for the sandwich that dropped on the floor and Duncan wiped clean before wrapping it in wax paper.

The sandwich route became an immediate success. In less than two hours Jeremy covered Hegeman, Hertzog, Ford, and Winants, cleaned out his baskets, and possessed a profit of two dollars for his evening's labors. When he returned to Spook's Hole Duncan already was there, and allowing for the fact that he had bought the last apple himself he had done as well as Jeremy.

"Dunc, we'll be rolling in wealth as this thing builds up."

"You do the shopping tomorrow."

"All right," Jeremy agreed, not liking the idea. "We didn't anywhere near cover the whole campus tonight."

"No, but one basket an evening is all I'm going to peddle."

"But why couldn't we hire a couple of other students to sell for us on a commission basis?"

"That's a thought."

In the end it proved to be a bad one. Ollie Darby, who lived over on the College of Agriculture campus, sold for three nights on a commission basis but barely made expenses as far as his employers were concerned. Ollie's basket was never better than half sold; clearly there was a saturation point to a ten o'clock sandwich route. Jeremy and Duncan faced this fact honestly; there was just about twenty dollars a week to be made from the business working five nights a week, and they had to make it themselves.

"Ten bucks each a week pays the old woman downstairs and buys our meals," Jeremy said practically.

But next afternoon Duncan forgot to do the shopping, and the evening was a total loss to both of them. Bitter words passed between the partners, and the atmosphere in Spook's Hole remained brittle until lights were turned off.

III

Duncan, however, reformed. While there was no longer the illusion of big business that had colored the enterprise while Ollie Darby had been working for them, still they were getting ahead. October slipped into November and the routine of shopping, sandwich-making, basket-packing, price-haggling over the last sandwich, the smaller apples, the softer portions of ice cream grew into habit. The route took time, but it made money. Still, Duncan, first of the two, became sick of keeping his nose to the grindstone. Jeremy recognized that he was faced with a morale problem, and compromised the situation by promising they would share expenses with Patsy DiOrio in driving to Easton for the Lafayette game.

Now that week end was past and Jeremy was having a discouraging Monday night. As he came out of House Six, Hegeman, the sandwich basket felt heavy in his hands. At least six of his regular customers had been out, either to the movies or studying at the library; and there had been two complaints that the sandwiches weren't worth the price, the apples wormy. He hadn't come anywhere near covering expenses, and the thought of trudging on to Hertzog, to Ford, to Winants chilled his spirits. He was tired of making sandwiches in Mrs. Bridewell's attic, wrangling with shopkeepers over the prices of apples and boiled ham and sliced cheese, being tied down every evening to a routine, and for what? So that Duncan and he could go to the Lafayette game and blow thirty dollars each in an afternoon and evening! Three weeks of drudgery to make up what they had squandered in less than a day. What fools they had been!

The November night was frosty, and Jeremy shivered as he toiled up the cobbled driveway to Hertzog. He was glad when he gained the warmth of the hallway, and as he stood for a moment catching his breath the temptation was strong to chuck the sandwich basket into the waste bin and call it quits. But down the hall he saw a light in Robert Hare's room.

Hare lounged in an easy chair, his legs crossed on the desk, a book in his lap. With his toes coming through the seams of a pair of battered bedroom slippers, Hare looked the model of a chap who was living comfortably at college. His study was warm and snug and simply furnished with the desk, a bookcase, two chairs and a dresser on which he had scattered his shaving things; Jeremy looked in upon the scene with obvious envy, and the envy lingered as Jeremy's gaze wandered to the photograph of Margery propped against a volume on differential calculus.

Quick to notice Jeremy's eyes on the photograph, Hare seemed pleased. "A sweet girl, Jeremy; I still can't believe she's willing to marry me. I've been sitting here reading Suckling and thinking about her. Ever read much Suckling, Jeremy? These lines somehow are exactly Margery to me—

"Her feet beneath her petticoat
Like little mice, stole in and out,
As if they feared the light;
But oh, she dances such a way!
No sun upon an Easter-day
Is half so fine a sight!"

Jeremy set down the sandwich basket. If Hare hadn't told him the source, he wouldn't have recognized the quotation from Suckling. Hare apparently read poetry avidly, and wrote verses himself that were published in *The Anthologist,* the college literary rag; Jeremy had thought Hare's verses rather good but was hesitant to say so for fear that Hare, like Whiskers, would lecture him on the curse of facility. Instead he took the anthology of poetry from Hare's lap and began thumbing through its pages.

"I wish I had time for stuff like this."

"If you can't find time for it in college, maybe you never will."

"I guess I started wrong. Somehow I'm always getting involved—*Targum*, the Barbarians, and now this sandwich route."

Hare said, "You were lucky, too. With this bad heart I always figured I had to get the most out of every minute, not knowing how long the minutes were going to last."

"None of us knows that," Jeremy said. But college only lasted four years, and they passed quickly. Hare was getting more out of the ivy years than he—getting it where it counted most, within himself. Hare and Margery—it was strange he should think of them both at the moment a stanza on the opened page caught his glance. With a smile he read aloud:

> "*Unless you can muse in a crowd all day*
> *On the absent face that fixed you;*
> *Unless you may love, as the angels may,*
> *With the breath of heaven betwixt you;*
> *Unless you can dream that his faith is fast,*
> *Through behoving and unbehoving;*
> *Unless you can die when the dream is past—*
> *Oh, never call it loving!*"

Hare laughed. "That's Browning," he said. "Lizzie, of course—not Robert."

"How many of them can you tell just by hearing them?"

"Most of them, I think."

Jeremy wanted to try again. He picked a page at random and read the first lines his eyes encountered:

> "*This bud of love, by summer's ripening breath,*
> *May prove a beauteous flower when next we meet.*"

"Shakespeare," Hare said. "Act II of *Romeo and Juliet*, just to prove I'm a real stuffed shirt."

Jeremy poured over the pages and tried once more:

> *"My only books*
> *Were woman's looks*
> *And folly's all they taught me."*

"Old Thomas Moore," Hare said. "And tolerably good advice."

A feeling of insufficiency kept growing within Jeremy. What had he gained from his books and classes to compare to this? Hare was having fun, and poetry had become alive for him, an intimate companion with whom he could share his solitude on a common ground of happy understanding. What more could a college education give?

Unhappy, dissatisfied, Jeremy laid the book on the desk and Robert Hare reached for it. The eagerness with which the boy in the battered bedroom slippers turned the pages revealed that he was looking for a favorite passage. His eyes were bright when after a moment he paused, reading silently, a smile on his lips. Then he said, "I don't suppose you have much time for Wordsworth, but these lines are so beautiful, they seem to say so much, that I'd like to read them to you."

"I wish you would." Jeremy simply forgot that time was passing and he still must peddle his wares in Ford and Winants if he wanted to break even on the night's enterprise.

"I'll try to read this thing with the feeling it deserves, not that I can, of course. Anyhow, it's from Wordsworth's 'Lines Written Above Tintern Abbey'—

> *"For I have learned*
> *To look on nature, not as in the hour*
> *Of thoughtless youth; but hearing often times*
> *The still, sad music of humanity,*
> *Nor harsh nor grating, though of ample power*
> *To chasten and subdue. And I have felt*
> *A presence that disturbs me with the joy*
> *Of elevated thoughts; a sense sublime*
> *Of something far more deeply interfused*

Whose dwelling is the light of setting suns,
And the round ocean and the living air,
And the blue sky, and in the mind of man;
A motion and a spirit that impels
All thinking things, all objects of all thought,
And rolls through all things. Therefore am I still
A lover of the meadows and the woods,
And mountains; and of all that we behold
From this green earth; of all the mighty world
Of eye, and ear,—both what they half create
And half perceive; well pleased to recognize
In nature and the language of the sense,
The anchor of my purest thoughts, the nurse,
The guide, and guardian of my heart, and soul
Of all my moral being."

Jeremy, listening, caught the beautiful cadence of the lines, but grasped only in part the thought. Still, he was deeply stirred, if only by the music of the words, and he thought: "This is right—college should mean moments like this."

"That's the genius of insight," Hare said, still holding the book. "As Shelley said it should, that's making 'poetry lift the veil from the hidden beauty of the world.'"

Almost with resentment Jeremy's eyes came back to the sandwich basket by his feet. He wanted to linger and yet he couldn't. Hare plainly hated to see him go and to prove it bought a sandwich and two apples.

Jeremy finished his rounds in Hertzog and trudged down the driveway toward Ford. He was missing the real part of college. First Whiskers and now Robert Hare were showing him that his education was only a veneer. He was missing too much, missing it forever. There was no glamor in working at college, in taking time from studies and dissipating the opportunities for companionship and intellectual adventure so that you could have a little extra money for an out-of-town football game or a prom week end. Remembering Robert Hare, comfortable and happy back in Hertzog, he saw himself as a fool, out here on a cold night lugging a sandwich basket. He thought of Creeper Bigelow, who, heaven knew, had been forced to scrape for every nickel to have the wherewithal to eat. But what really had Creeper gained from college? Creeper's education at best had been surface deep, and even Creeper, so desperately hard up for money, had pinched for the luxury of belonging to a fraternity.

"The poor dumb cluck," Jeremy muttered.

IV

In the morning Robert Hare was dead. Jeremy learned this shocking news on his way to Twissy's eleven o'clock class in literary criticism. The details, as Muggsy supplied them, were meager; Hare's bad heart had given out while he slept; when the woman had come in to make the bed he had already been dead for some hours.

Jeremy sat through Twissy's lecture, stunned and unheeding. His mind seemed alive with memories of Robert Hare: the rehearsals a year ago for Skit Night, the evening Hare had decided to join a fraternity, the day after Olanski's suicide when Creeper and he had interviewed Hare, last night when Hare had read the passage from Wordsworth. Jeremy simply couldn't stop thinking about the classmate who an evening ago had appeared so alive and vital, and now was lost forever save in the minds and hearts of a few who had known and loved him.

About Robert Hare, in retrospect, there seemed so much of wholeness, and of good, hard common sense. So much honesty too—intellectual honesty, a rare attribute in a man at any age. Robert Hare had spoken frankly of his weak heart, but not uncheerfully or bitterly, for he had been more concerned with living. But life was perishable; the ivy years were perishable; to waste one day of them, to throw away one opportunity or to ignore one adventure that they offered was to remain impoverished by that margin all the rest of your life. Jeremy had sensed this truth last night, but now it had been brought home to him with the terrible impact of death.

The class ended and Jeremy walked directly to Old Queen's, hoping to find the dean of men in his office.

"It was too bad about Hare," the dean said, seeming to know what was on the other's mind.

Jeremy nodded dully. He told the dean about the previous evening in Hare's room, about Spook's Hole and the sandwich route, about the thirty dollars thrown away at the Lafayette game.

"What do you want, Jeremy?"

"I want to borrow some money."

"How much?"

"Enough to go back to Hegeman and to cut out wasting my time working now while I am in college.

"What will you do next year?"

"Borrow the money where I can."

The dean drummed his fingers on the desk. "I think you're worth a small scholarship—say, a hundred dollars a year. And the Student Loan Fund will stake you to as much more as you need, for this year at least."

"Thank you, sir."

Jeremy, coming back onto the campus, paused to look up through the leafless old trees. It was not as though he was seeing them for the first time, but merely that he was seeing them with new meaning. The ivy years were more than half gone; he had lost ground to regain. Then, though hunger pangs assailed him, he set out in search of Muggsy, for it seemed only sporting to inform Muggsy that he had recently acquired a roommate.

8

"TO HIGHER FIELDS"

I

For two years Jeremy had been perfectly willing to keep a safe distance between Dr. Will and himself. There really had been no reason for them to meet more than once a year—when, as a matter of college regulation, it became necessary for every undergraduate to consult with his faculty adviser concerning his courses for the coming year—and Jeremy had been entirely satisfied with this arrangement. Before such meetings Jeremy assured himself that Will was a harmless old goat, but the moment he walked into the man's office the unhappy memory of their first interview revived his latent resentment, and he was ill at ease until the conferences ended. But in the junior year Jeremy's professional courses in journalism began; Dr. Will was no longer escapable; Jeremy had come to the time when he must exhibit himself eight hours of every week before the man's gaze and wonder uncomfortably at what instant Will would decide the affliction had not improved sufficiently to permit Jeremy's continuance in the curriculum.

Dr. Will was civil and considerate in his attitude toward Jeremy; he could see that the boy was handicapped in the class in copy-editing, marking the dispatches from the Associated Press teletype either too heavily or almost illegibly, but he never commented on that fact; and yet Jeremy knew that he noticed and never met Will's gaze or Will's smile without a sense of tight defensiveness. All of Will's kindly indulgence went for naught; whenever the two of them were in the same room, Jeremy remembered the fable of the cat that had played with the mouse and even fancied he detected a feline softness in his instructor's manner; Will in a halo with wings at his shoulders still would have been unconvincing. Nothing better than a truce existed between them, and at any moment the explosion might come. Jeremy was no fool; an afflicted person had to be sensitive to the threat of danger, becoming forearmed by being forewarned, or else he was lost forever.

But despite the uncomfortable premonitions that Will's presence aroused in Jeremy, his classes in journalism claimed many pleasant aspects. With his previous experience in newspaper work and the training Billy Farrand had pounded into him on *The Targum,* the courses in news reporting and editorial writing came easily and created the illusion of playing at newspaper work rather than of actually preparing for it. He became convinced at the end of a month that he was wasting most of the time he devoted to his journalism classes; he was frankly contemptuous of journalism *per se* as the basis of a college curriculum, believing that the writing of a news story or the mechanics of marking copy were subjects that any intelligent student might pick up in a few hours; but he remained in the curriculum and not alone for the fact that not to do so would seem to be heeling before Will. The classes were coeducational—the only classes in the university that enrolled students both from the men's colleges and the College for Women—and Jeremy was not unresponsive to the attractive possibilities thereby provided. But in this respect Jeremy discovered that the classroom was not a setting for romance, especially late in the afternoon when make-ups wore thin, hair-dos grew scraggly, and the competition of recitation either condemned the bright girl for knowing too much or the stupid one for becoming a bore. In the end Jeremy eliminated the presence of the women students as a reason for remaining in journalism; more to the point was the fact that his professional courses entailed practically no outside studying and thus gave him more leisure than he had enjoyed since the beginning of the ivy years. This circumstance was tremendously appealing, particularly after Robert Hare's death led Jeremy to quit Spook's Hole and to resolve that he would live at college with some intellectual awareness of what each day could offer. At no better time and in no better spirit could he have come under the influence of Houston Peterson.

For a generation undergraduates had been calling Dr. Peterson "Pete," and Jeremy fell at once into the habit. After one week in philosophy he was telling Muggsy that Pete was the brains and class and personality of the faculty. Jeremy had never known anyone like Pete; the man sparkled with charm and made his learning more glamorous than a Hollywood starlet's curves, no small accomplishment for a medium-sized, ruddy-cheeked, rather roly poly academician over thirty-five. But Jeremy could not have described Pete in terms of width and height and frame and girth. Pete's mustache, of course, made an impression, but even that feature was not what Jeremy remembered first when he thought of Pete. A pair of eyes brimming over with fun and liveliness and intelligence—that was Pete. And other pictures abounded: Pete in front of a class sitting on a corner of a desk, puffing a cigarette with a quick, nervous absent-mindedness, tamping out one, lighting another with the telltale, habit-bred nonchalance of the chain-smoker; Pete with a book in his hand, reading from Spinoza or Hegel or James or Santanyana, the lilt of poetry in his voice; Pete lecturing with chalk from the blackboard in smears on his coat, his heart so obviously in the task, his adeptness for quotation a source of constant astonishment; Pete on the campus, a bustling little man in a black fedora hat who swung a brown brief case as he walked along trailed by a coterie of smarties like Whiskers.

Pete was Gulliver. Pete was Quixote. Jeremy reasoned practically that Pete had to be good to teach on three faculties at the same time—Rutgers, Columbia, and Cooper Union. Pete had to be mentally alive to write the kind of books that were published under his name—*The Melody of Chaos; Havelock Ellis, Philosopher of Love; Huxley, Prophet of Science*. But most of all Pete was regular—a man who talked football or baseball as glibly as the naturalism of Herbert Spencer or the mythological symbolism of Schopenhauer. In the final analysis, Pete, who had corrected galley proofs on his latest book while attending a six-day bicycle race because he liked noise and excitement and people, stood alone.

Muggsy looked with disdain at the pile of books Jeremy had carted back to Hegeman after an afternoon rummaging among the stacks of a dealer in used books. A dog-eared copy of Plato's *Republic* left Muggsy entirely unimpressed, although he agreed with the inscription written on the flyleaf by a previous owner: "Morons are happiest in college." The yellowed pages of the six volumes of *The Collected Works of Thomas Hood* struck him as virtually unreadable, considering their small print. The copy of DeQuincey's *Confessions of an English Opium Eater* had a nice title page and red poppies on the cover, but Muggsy's appetite for opium eating was satisfied by these cursory foretastes.

"I picked up the lot of them for sixty-five cents," Jeremy announced with pride.

"What do you want 'em for?"

"To read, you sap!"

Muggsy shook his head. He didn't believe that Jeremy was going to read this stuff any more than he had read the thirteen volumes of Ibsen bought in his freshman year.

"How do you know you aren't carrying in a lot of diseases on these old books?" he asked critically.

Jeremy exploded irritably. "I hope I am. I just hope you get syphillis handling them. And I hope I'm around when you try to explain to your dad that it must have come from a *book!*"

Muggsy looked pained, and Jeremy fondled his soiled and mutilated books with a tender touch. It had been fun sorting through the piles of books in the old shop on George Street, haggling over prices, driving down the price on the set of Hood to forty cents, getting the DeQuincey for a nickel. Muggsy doubtless considered the writings of Hood and De-Quincey as dead ducks, but not Pete. Pete could quote from anybody as though he lived right across the hall in Pete's Greenwich Village apartment and had come over in his shirttail that morning for a cup of coffee. Pete preached no gospel more convincingly than the kingdom of books. Pete said it wasn't the binding that made a book valuable, but simply whether you owned the book and could lay hands on it when the urge seized you. Beg, borrow, or steal your books, but own your own books, build a personal library, have books within arm's reach wherever you lived.

"I'll give a prize—ten dollars, a lot of money for a college professor—to the student who builds the best personal library before the year is out," Pete had said in class the day before.

With classes at Columbia and Cooper Union as well as at Rutgers, Pete had to teach and run; instead of teaching philosophy one hour each on Monday, Wednesday, and Friday, he covered the week's work in one two-hour session on Wednesday afternoon. The overlong period should have been disasterously tiresome and tedious, but Pete kept it lively. With laughter. With ideas. With his own rules for getting the most out of college.

"Now this textbook," Pete said in his first lecture, "isn't much good. In graduate seminar I sat next to the chap who wrote it. He wasn't any brighter than the rest of us, but he wrote a book first."

Somehow Jeremy felt more at ease with that textbook; Pete had this gift of making the whole educative experience comfortably personal. A book that simply belonged to the author, Pete taught, wasn't a book to value. If you wanted a book to belong to you, then you had to contribute part of yourself to that book. As you read you jotted down in the margin ideas and conclusions that occurred to you, and when you had finished the volume you made your own index to these special references. "That book is yours then," Pete said. "It is actually recreated through your own mind."

Pete was a tough marker and cheerfully admitted it. He made a point of speaking a friendly aside to those in his classes who were involved in outside activities. "You fellows are smart," he said. "You've learned something about college that some chaps never learn. You can play when you're tired, but a tired man can't study." Like the rest, Jeremy nodded, but he didn't really believe that he was hoodwinking Pete; when to play and when to study wasn't something he had learned, but he knew that he had better learn it if he wanted to pass philosophy.

Pete's class was the most demanding of all the courses Jeremy studied during the ivy years, and yet it was easily his favorite and the one course that he considered contributed the most to his intellectual development. The enjoyment of permitting his mind to roam through the realm of pure presuppositions—the essence of mathematics which he had never grasped—he encountered once more in Pete's lectures on logic and ethics. Darwinism again came forth to challenge his innate mysticism, but now he read Darwin's *Voyage of the Beagle* and *Descent of Man* and at least could argue with some degree of confidence in his background. As much as anything philosophy taught him tolerance; no ideology, including the Christian ideology, ever had swept the world and obviously never would; to cling to one's own ideals while conceding the other fellow dignity in holding to his was, perhaps, the basic test of a civilized mind. Or, in reverse, Jeremy was learning to be more indulgent toward dogmatism in others and less indulgent toward dogmatism in himself. It was not a lesson that he mastered at once or possibly has mastered to this day; but at least Pete revealed that the lesson existed to be learned, and in the light of that knowledge Jeremy felt wiser.

II

Philosophy called for a prodigious amount of outside reading, but Pete knew what he was doing; he made a deliberate point of driving his students into the university library. It was only a matter of time before they would grow used to the musty odor that invariably attached itself to old books, and, in a milder degree, to those who handled them. There was even something to be gained from observing the tip-toed tread of the library assistants as they moved from one task to another like habitual somnambulists; meekness had never been unworthy approaches to the treasures of learning. But even more important was the discovery of what the library actually represented: the beating heart behind the entire university.

Jeremy had been coming to the library three afternoons a week for better than a month. Pete had set him to reading the German philosophers, and he was finding them excessively heavy and dull; an hour curled over the table in one of the reading booths seemed the limit of his endurance with the moralistic writings of Fichte; then he switched off the light and enjoyed the luxury of leaving the books piled on the table for some attendant to carry back to the stacks. But he was in no hurry to return to Hegeman. Now he was a free spirit; now he could prowl through the stacks where fancy led him; now he could linger over a book for no better reason than the fact that the title or the binding took his eye. For a month he had browsed in this mood of carefree escape, and the rewards had been pleasant. At first he had been staggered by the hundreds of thousands of books that surrounded him; if a man read twenty hours a day for a lifetime, he could not read all the important books in print; but gradually Jeremy realized that he was becoming familiar with the broad arrangements of a catalogued collection of books, and there was a reassuring sense of power in that revelation. As long as he knew where to seek, the wisdom of the centuries was within his grasp. And kinds of books he had never dreamed existed came before his fascinated gaze: local histories, yellowed travelogues, works on pottery-making, religious customs, welding, sailboating, novel writing, advertising, mosquito control, African tribal dances. He carried back to the dormitory a book on diseases of the stomach and tormented Muggsy into hitherto unimagined agonies of hypochondria.

The library took on a life of its own, and Jeremy enjoyed being absorbed into it as part observer, part participant. Sooner or later every afternoon he was certain to meet old Dr. Kirk prowling through the stacks, not among the books in Greek, but among the collections on military history or early Americana. The man possessed a shy smile, but he knew Jeremy at sight by now. Or in the last reading booth on the lower level Jeremy could be reasonably sure of finding the boy and girl who came there shortly before four in the afternoon; sometimes they held hands while they studied, sometimes the girl put her head on her arms and fell asleep, sometimes she rested her head on the boy's shoulder; she was a frail little thing who wore plaid skirts and low-heeled oxfords, and her brown eyes held softness and warmth and depth. Three booths away the table and chair belonged to the crotchety old gentleman who came at three o'clock every Tuesday and Thursday; the man appeared to grumble whenever students pounded down the stairs, and muttered an angry *"Sshsh!"* if they dared to converse above a whisper; he looked as if he hadn't a red corpuscle remaining in his blood or a bit of fun in his being, but Jeremy watched the books he read—tomes on bull-fighting. Jeremy refused to be surprised; the library was like that, a place where the unexpected lurked around practically every corner. It was like a great human grab bag without a bottom.

And Jeremy was himself part of that grab bag; one day he might reach in and pull out the astonishing fact that old Dr. Kirk read military history with an avid interest, but the next the discovery could just as reasonably reveal some unexpected facet in the personality of Jeremy Baxter.

"You're a blooming sensualist toward books," he told himself one afternoon, and grinned at the possible implications that the Freudian psychologists could attach to this admission. But the fact remained: some books felt pleasant to his touch and others did not, a matter of size and weight and physical proportions; some title pages struck him with a sense of wonder at the beauty of their arrangement, and others depressed his spirit by reflecting nothing more than the hack work of the mechanical craftsman. Jeremy refused to believe that some hidden childhood frustration was at the bottom of his newly found interest in the physical characteristics of books; more likely his native aptitude for type arrangement manifest when he had guided Hell Box in making up the pages of *The Targum* was grasping the wider, more fascinating possibilities of topography in its relation to bookmaking. He wanted to know more.

The library bookstacks did not disappoint him. Books on the history of printing in the main were ponderous and stuffy reading, but their illustrations were enthralling: sharp-nosed Aldus Manutius of Venice, the testy little tutor who had been inspired by the vision of giving the Greek and Latin classics to the world in printed instead of in written form; John Baskerville's vigorous and perfectly proportioned title pages ("Printed jet black," Jeremy thought, "as God intended that type should be put on paper!"); Bodoni's type specimen

pages as set by his own unerring hand. The romance of printing and bookmaking filled his head and heart; he read books
on type cutting, type setting, type design; and names like
Caslon, Garamond, Goudy, and Updike became part of his
mental life, strangers except to those in the compact little
world that knew and loved them. Printing and bookmaking
were not trades; they were arts. Jeremy sometimes was lost in
daydreams of owning a private press where nothing but fine
books were printed.

His interest in printing and bookmaking had not passed
unnoticed by the members of the library staff. The woman at
the loan desk said unexpectedly one day, "There's a new
book in from the Merrymount Press. Want to see it?"

Jeremy nodded eagerly; the Merrymount Press was Updike, unquestionably one of the best contemporary printers
in America. The book was no disappointment; the Updike
pages had a splendid, rich blackness as though Baskerville
himself had printed them. Jeremy studied the new Merrymount title with his heart beating happily; but his pleasure
was no greater than that of the woman who had recognized
his interest. And after that whenever he came into the library
there were other books held out for him to see: examples of
Bruce Rogers's impeccable craftsmanship, some of the fine
books Carl Purington Rollins had designed at Yale and Fred-
eric Warde at Princeton. Jeremy studied them all, grateful,
excited, his pride expanding at the knowledge that his judgments on books was not only being cultivated but also sought.
"How does this strike you?" a library assistant would ask,
stopping him in the hall and handing him a book. Jeremy
would appraise it carefully; he liked the feeling of being accepted as a pseudo-expert and had no wish of spoiling the
game with a hasty, foolish decision.

His afternoons in the library were becoming richer, more
gratifying adventures, even though he seemed to be weaned
away more and more from reading for Pete's course in phi-

losophy. Had he seen the new exhibit of eighteenth century books in the show cases in the museum? Jeremy spent the afternoon examining the books, and the librarian, a quiet, bald-headed little man who sometimes stood by the side door puffing on his pipe, came over stuffing the still hot pipe bowl in his pocket.

"Let me open the cases for you. That's an original Webster speller there. Do you know how to spell?"

Jeremy confessed that he didn't—not very well.

"Well, neither do I," the librarian said. "That's why a man has a secretary . . . for that, and to cover up his ignorance in a lot of other ways."

The case was opened. Jeremy handled the books and discussed them with the librarian. He rarely had known a happier afternoon.

The following day the librarian's secretary stopped him in the hall. "Mr. Osborn wanted me to point out this item in a dealer's catalogue. There's a Kelmscott Press book here that looks rather good. Do you think we should consider getting it?"

"Why, I—" Jeremy knew the book was probably an excellent one. "Yes, I think you should consider it."

The secretary thanked him. Jeremy's heart was warm. He stood, still glowing at the flattery implied in the librarian's interest in his opinion, when a voice spoke over his shoulder.

"I've noticed you around here a lot lately. It doesn't make sense to me."

Since leaving Spook's Hole, Jeremy hadn't thought once of Whiskers.

"You don't think I make a convincing grind?"

"No more convincing than I'd be running the Junior Prom."

Jeremy smiled. The temptation to impress Whiskers with his recently acquired knowledge became irresistible. But Whiskers was interested and wanted to know more. Jeremy

was delighted to share his enthusiasm; he walked down
College Avenue as far as Bartlett Street, telling Whiskers
what he had learned.

"Why don't you design books if you like it so much?"

"With the shakes?"

"Why not? You can always tell somebody else how to
execute your ideas. You could even tell me."

"Would you?"

"Of course!"

Jeremy walked back to Hegeman, shaking his head. Why
did an afflicted person always have to be such an infernal
boob, bottling himself up within himself? He felt as though
Whiskers had become his warmest friend.

But Jeremy, converted from animosity to friendship toward Whiskers, still could not escape a sense of uneasiness
in Whiskers's presence. It was simply a matter of an inferior-
ity complex, Jeremy supposed; but he couldn't be sure that
this was the sole cause of his discomfiture. Accepting Whiskers also meant accepting Whiskers's friends—Julius Lang,
in particular. A tall, gaunt, angular chap with a sharp nose,
a fuzzy mustache, and a receding chin, Julius lived by himself
in a room above Louie's restaurant on Somerset Street.
Julius was easily the most unattractive boy Jeremy knew; his
voice was high-pitched and nasal, his wit barbed, his manner
brusque; but Whiskers and Julius were inseparable, and so
Jeremy tried to be friendly also. He went to Julius's room
late one January afternoon when the weather suddenly
turned mild and the snow on Somerset Street was trans-
formed into dirty slush. An iron bed, a pine bureau with
neckties hanging over the mirror, a rickety table with an old
Oliver typewriter, and a pair of equally rickety chairs com-
prised the room's entire furnishings; the floor was bare and
apparently had been unswept for some time, but there was
little wonder for that—piles of books were everywhere, forming aisles between the bed and the bureau, the door and the

table, the closet, and the chair on which Julius's pajamas lay where they had been thrown that morning.

Whiskers, curling up on the bed, seemed undisturbed by the unkemptness of the place. Jeremy sat in the chair by the table, obviously the guest chair, and Julius sat on the window sill.

"Jeremy's interested in bookmaking," Whiskers said, and Jeremy felt uncomfortable, as though the respectability of his birth was being vouched for.

"The hand-illuminated manuscript books were gorgeous," Julius said. "They have some of them on exhibit at the New York Public Library."

"I know the ones you mean," Whiskers said. "They're up on the third floor."

Jeremy resolved to see the exhibit next time he was in the city. Julius looked down onto the street.

"Pete said he might stop in."

"What's on his mind?" Whiskers asked.

"A new idea for a book."

Jeremy wondered if he were being spoofed. Why should Pete want to come up to this rat's nest, and why should he confide in any undergraduate about the heavy stuff he wrote? But Jeremy was glad that he hadn't put these questions to his comrades, for within five minutes Pete's quick, nervously impatient tread sounded on the stairs. He didn't appear the least concerned that there was only one chair which Jeremy now occupied with some embarrassment; he seemed thoroughly comfortable sitting on a pile of books.

"I come like Hamlet, Julius, to ask the same old question: 'To be or not to be.' "

"Is that your book idea?"

"A book about the place of the soliloquy in life and literature. Why is Hamlet's 'to be or not to be' immortal, if not for the fact that the soliloquy is a life form, especially characteristic of a perturbed, distracted civilization?"

"Is it?" Whiskers demanded.

"It is. Every individual in a moment of great trouble or confusion must make his own decision. Often his light fails him, his faith fails him. He falls back into himself, cut off from society, nature, God. And then begins the lonely debate which everyone knows but only the great writer can put into recognizable language."

Julius nodded. "Like Shakespeare. Remember Macbeth? The climax seems to be the bloody murder of Duncan, but isn't the climax actually hidden in the soliloquy of the first act:

> " 'If it were done when 'tis done, then 'twere well
> It were done quickly.'?"

"Shakespeare's plays are filled with such speeches," Pete said. "Again and again he leaves his characters alone on the stage—to muse, to dream, to deliberate. Corneille and Racine do the same with their heroes; Goethe with Faust, Ibsen with Peer Gynt."

Julius broke in, "Don't forget Zola's Doctor Pascal."

"Or Ahab sitting alone by the stern windows in *Moby Dick*," Whiskers suggested.

Pete laughed. "You find examples everywhere—in literature as in life. Think of some of the great characters whose soliloquies are unforgettable . . . Figaro, Emperor Jones, Robinson Crusoe, the Great God Brown. A person can say things to himself that he can say to no one else—not even to his psychoanalyst. Honor, prudence, fear, shame, remorse, stand in the way of communication with one's fellows. Timidity makes candor difficult—social taboos may make it hazardous or impossible. So the subtle artist releases the tongues of his fictitious characters—whom we know to be ourselves."

Jeremy was content simply to listen. Pete plunged on enthusiastically—where else but in the soliloquy could you find the logic of Aristotle so completely mixed up with the logic of passion? Jeremy shook his head. The discussion was beginning to run deeper, and he already felt out of his depth. But it was somehow exciting. Whiskers had rolled over on the bed, his chin resting on his hands, listening. Julius twisted his foot behind the radiator and seemed to understand every word Pete was saying. Jeremy stored away in his mind the scene the four of them made in that little room above Louie's restaurant. He thought of it as an oldtime lithograph: "The Birth Pangs of a Book." Or, perhaps more accurately: "The Ivy Years—An Incident."

Walking home alone, he thought with a chuckle, "All right, they asked for it. I'll soliloquize about them." Pete, first: a man with a mind that tried to keep touch with everything and everybody, a real teacher. Could he be like Pete? Jeremy lingered on the thought hopefully, and then surrendered. He'd never have Pete's overall grasp of knowledge; he had started wrong or started late, depending on how you chose to look at it. In some things he might be like Pete, an intellectual; but not in everything, as Pete appeared to be. Not that he might not hold his own with Pete on the matter of bookmaking. Jeremy was satisfied to dismiss Pete with his own ego partly rescued on that reflection.

How about Whiskers and Julius then? Again he had to admit they were ahead of him, and probably always would be. At least he could concede that a grind was not without some enviable virtues. But Julius and Whiskers missed a good part of college, too. He couldn't feel warm toward them, not the way he felt toward Muggsy. He wasn't really at ease with them; their fun was all up in their heads, and he wasn't made that way. But there were more Muggsys in the world than Juliuses or Whiskerses. Perhaps somewhere in between a firm middle ground existed.

Jeremy hoped so, for there was where he was heading. If Will gave him respectable grades in journalism, he'd make the honor school, and he wanted to. If he could have awakened mentally just a year sooner, he might have had a chance for Phi Beta Kappa. Not knowing how to study, too much cutting up, too much talking about girls, *Targum*, the Barbarians, the sandwich route had all held him back. But he wasn't sorry it had worked that way; he had gained education from those experiences also—perhaps a broader education in getting along with his fellow man than either Whiskers or Julius could claim.

III

Silvers said, "I don't know Julius Lang, or Whiskers either, but you can't tell about grinds. Some of them are never heard of after college, but others become our most famous alumni. A well developed mind counts, but as Jeremy says, you've still got to be able to live with people, to enjoy them, be part of them."

Muggsy said, "Julius Lang has halitosis."

Jeremy said, "You ought to see Muggsy's collection of patent medicines. He believes all the ads about pink toothbrush and b.o."

Silvers laughed. "This is supposed to be a class in short story writing."

There wasn't another class in college like it, Jeremy admitted. The six juniors who met once a week in Silvers's office discussed anything that pleased their fancy. Muggsy and Jeremy had been forced to secure Dr. Will's permission to take the course; the journalism department head had given in grudgingly, grumbling that he didn't see what short story writing had to do with newspaper work; and Jeremy suspected that Will wouldn't have capitulated if he hadn't been afraid of Silvers. The class was conducted in an informal and completely democratic manner; the six juniors sat around Silvers's desk, chairs tipped back, feet braced against the desk itself; and Professor Silvers, placing a large gold

watch on the desk, proceeded to talk for an hour. Sometimes
he lectured on writing the short story, but more often he did
not. He was as likely to give over the hour to telling them
about Ruthie, his secretary, who had fallen in love, then
fallen out of love, but now had fallen in love again. Or
about Dr. Demarest, who had been president of the college
when Professor Silvers had first come to work at Rutgers,
and who had been so honest that he had kept separate groups
of postage stamps in his desk, one for personal mail and one
for official mail, and who, whenever he wrote a letter that
was both personal and official, paid the postage out of his
own pocket. The class followed none of the rules of orthodox
pedagogy, and yet no one of the six juniors ever cut one of
its sessions. And somehow the instruction was successful, because before the year ended four of the students sold short
stories. Jeremy was one of them; a church school publication
paid him fifteen dollars for a football story with a college
setting, and his head was in the clouds. Perhaps what Silvers
demonstrated was that in the teaching of writing theory was
unimportant when humanity itself could be used for a textbook.

Silvers's class in short story writing, meeting only one hour
a week and requiring no more outside preparation than the
professional courses in journalism, contributed three credit
hours toward Jeremy's baccalaureate degree but further protected his leisure. Even with the outside reading required
for Pete's course in philosophy or for Lizzie Whitman's
course in contemporary drama, Jeremy had the time to do
as he pleased. There were, of course, the editorials to write
for *The Targum,* but they took only an hour or two twice
a week, and there were badgered freshmen underlings at
hand to do the really dirty work. Jeremy could be glad he
had stuck by *The Targum* system, for it was serving him
well; a freshman carried his editorial to the printer, fetched
the proof, waited while it was read through and corrected,

then raced back to place the mutilated masterpiece into the hands of a cynical Hell Box. But Jeremy played fair with his conscience; he never once stooped to writing an editorial about keeping off the campus grass or getting out to support that Big Red Team.

Freed from mathematics, a foreign language, and the sciences, Jeremy's studies were all in line with his interests. Journalism, of course, was his major—the thing by which he was supposed in later years to earn his bread and butter. But somehow his coming problems as a wage slave did not seem insistent; an engineer or chemist or ceramist was stuck with his professional labs, even an education major had to put in his licks of practice teaching or an aggie his hours at the College Farm; but the liberal arts student had no task more pressing than the cultivation of his own mind. Jeremy could not say that he regretted the choice he had made; he could live with books, or he could simply loaf, or he could let his mind roam through the fascinating thoroughfares of fancy. A deep satisfaction was growing in him, compounded of little things that were part of his day by day existence: the reading of a Hardy novel, an editorial written for *The Targum* that seemed to have a flavor of expression not uninfluenced by a growing intimacy with the style of Emerson, a walk along the footpath that divided river from canal while he thought of God and girls and Thoreau and Pete and the coming Junior Prom, an afternoon with Muggsy planning a new show to Gilbert and Sullivan tunes that they would stage in the University cafeteria some night for nonfraternity men, an evening in the library browsing, coming upon a history of the Indian wars of Connecticut, and thinking (since just that afternoon he had been reading a novel by Kenneth Roberts) that he might like trying to write a historical novel some day. In the liberal arts tradition, his mind was open to an endless succession of schemes and hopes and dreams; he read Ibsen and Racine and Moliere for Lizzie Whitman and toyed with an urge to be a playwright; Silvers lectured on the stories of Chekov and De Maupassant and Maugham and Marquand and he wanted to write short stories; Pete set him to reading Santayana and he dreamed of being a philosopher who found faith and strength and wisdom through understanding the suffering insecurity of humanity; Will, giving the class the problem of arranging news stories on a dummy front page, filled him with the ambition to devise a new format for a newspaper, something more compact than the standard eight-column page, easier to hold and to read without the garishness of too many bold faced headlines. He enjoyed the elasticity that had come to his mind; he could feel himself growing mentally as his interests broadened; and education became like pollen upon a wind, falling upon the rich seed of his imagination, fertilizing and cross-fertilizing, and creating day after day new insights, new ideas, new enthusiasms. With leisure and mental awakening came the equally pleasant discovery of how to study—with his feet on the desk, relaxed, his mind alert to the sentence or thought that more or less summed up the whole section of a chapter. They were the sentences and thoughts to remember, and the rest of the stuff was usually window dressing—window dressing a bit on the shoddy side at that. Pete had given the right answer: study while you were rested, for you were never too tired for fun, anyhow.

Life suddenly had never seemed more pleasant. Jeremy had quit eating in Hertzog and went every night for his meal at the cafeteria. A group of his friends sat with him every evening—Muggsy, Duncan Faust, sometimes Whiskers and Julius, and on party week ends when the fraternities were filled with guests, Iron Man and Jack. Iron Man was a three-letter winner now, and a scarlet R glistened on his sweatered chest; but Iron Man talked mostly about girls or his classes in Italian; the literature of his native tongue was the only real literature to Iron Man, and to prove it he would recite a canto from Dante at the first encouragement. Nobody else knew Italian and so Iron Man's recitations passed undisputed; he made them convincing by claiming that he knew more Italian than old Dutchy Davis, who taught the course and never had cooked raviola in all his life. Jeremy chuckled; it was wonderful having Iron Man turn intellectual, even unintelligibly intellectual. The student bus boys were piling the chairs on the tables and sweeping up for the night when the cafeteria dinner group disbanded; usually it was after eight by then, better than two hours since they had sat down; but what was time compared to fellowship?

It seemed to Jeremy that his junior year, beginning in Spook's Hole, almost going to pot because of a sandwich route, gaining purpose and perspective with Robert Hare's death, ripening into the full fruition of leisurely and contented studentship under the influence of Pete and Whiskers and the happy circumstance of eleven hours of classes requiring scant preparation, had become the richest of the ivy years. There appeared nothing better for them to bring. But Pete could have told Jeremy that he was wrong, and have quoted from Shakespeare to prove it—"our youth leads on to higher fields." In Jeremy's case the step ahead was love.

9

AGNES

I

Here's to love, its joy and fret,
May this bring solace and help you forget
The women you want and the women you get!

Muggsy's teeth chattered as he darted through the cold February night, reciting this toast that he had culled from a novel by T. S. Stribling. The casual passer-by, observing the habiliments in which Muggsy chose to brave one of the frostiest evenings of the winter, might well have despaired for the lad's sanity. Muggsy's feet were clad in bedroom slippers over which he had drawn a pair of rubbers; his legs were bare except where his overcoat swirled around his bony knees; he wore neither trousers nor coat and vest, but carried these articles in a bundle under his arm; and the derby on his head was definitely a size too big, for it slid over his ears and with every step seemed to bob up and down like the top of a steam valve. But to Muggsy there was nothing illogical in his predicament. When he reached Hertzog, he was going to press his tuxedo as soon as he could snatch his turn at the ironing board. The studs for his dress shirt were tied in a little bag that he carried for safe-keeping inside his derby. His bow tie was in his coat pocket; his shoes, just freshly shined, were wrapped inside his trousers. Half an hour hence when he emerged from the laundry of Hertzog, he expected to dazzle his contemporaries as a picture of sartorial excellence. The beau brummel of the junior prom— that is, if he could press a straight crease in his pants! Muggsy hurried on, agonized by this sudden fear.

For more than a month Muggsy had been living in anticipation of prom week. Muggsy lived for all the big social events on the college calendar: the soph hop in December, the prom in February, the military ball in May, and the senior ball in June. Muggsy stumbled, almost lost his derby, and stood for a moment rearranging his belongings. An icy blast swept down the path, seeming to congeal the marrow in his bones. Muggsy struggled on, numb and cold and disgusted with himself. He was the clumsiest ass in captivity, and he blamed his mother for it. She bossed him in everything, and so as a baby she had made him walk too soon, and he never had felt secure on his feet. Awkwardness had kept him off the tennis team—even from being ball boy, since whenever he attended a match he distracted the players by seeming in imminent danger of tripping over his own feet and falling flat on his face. His clumsiness made him ill at ease and quickly irritated; he would have done better as a student if he could have applied himself more diligently, but he would write a letter, and maybe compose a limerick, and study an assignment in history simultaneously. It was a form of mental stumbling, he knew, and the fault went back to the fact that they had made him walk before he was ready. And on a dance floor—Muggsy groaned to think of how the wax betrayed his feet and the awful feeling he suffered that his fanny hung out under his coat tails like a half-filled sack of potatoes.

But this week end Muggsy had high hopes. This was the week end he was going to rise above the curse on his life. He'd show the lot of 'em he was no kid. A big week end was ahead—the prom tonight, a basketball game and fraternity house parties tomorrow, chapel on Sunday morning—and he had plans. After the house parties tomorrow night, that would be the moment. In the taxi going home. He'd take his girl to the movies, then to the basketball game, then to the house parties. He wasn't going to wear his glasses this week end; they felt funny on his nose. In the taxi—that was the spot.

"Call me Muggsy, the leader of the wolf pack," he told himself jovially. He was almost to Hertzog and he wasn't sorry. Another half block and they'd have found him in the morning, frozen bright blue. He wondered if his turned-out navel had anything to do with his feeling the cold so badly.

II

Back in Hegeman Jeremy surveyed himself in the mirror. His neck felt too tight inside his collar; he fancied that the front of his dress shirt bulged; and his bow tie appeared to sag on one end, creating the impression that it had quarreled with his Adam's apple, had come off a bad second, and now chose to sulk for the remainder of the evening. Jeremy eyed the tie with hostility; he pushed it back into place, gently and prayerfully, and waited to see if it would sag. It sagged. Jeremy ripped the thing from his throat and hurled it out the window. If he ran he should find one haberdashery still open in town. Jeremy went out of Hegeman as though jet-propelled.

The cold night air made him shiver, and within a block his breath came in little puffs. The patent leather dance pumps that mom had insisted on buying pinched his feet; he felt foolish and sissified in them. Around him the campus seemed peaceful, but the appearance out of the shadows of an undergraduate hurrying on with a tuxedo on a hanger was evidence that Jeremy was not alone in his agitation. The way the other chap was carrying his tuxedo—straight out in front of him so that his eyes were glued on it every step

—told you he would have defended it with his life. The pair passed with a nod and Jeremy's mind came back to his own affairs.

Muggsy's girl was named Flo and his girl's name was Alice. Alice Evans. A pretty name, Jeremy decided; he wished he could remember better how she looked. She was blonde with blue eyes and not too tall. Her voice was low—maybe husky, if you were describing it in a novel. She was seventeen and lived down the road from Muggsy's family. Muggsy had gotten him the date with Alice; or rather Muggsy's mother, who was quite a manager in such things, had arranged it. "Why, she's just the dearest, sweetest little angel," Muggsy's mother had said. "You'll be a lucky boy to take her to the prom, Jeremy. She's a good girl from a very fine old family." Jeremy recalled Alice's recommendations with a slight tinge of uneasiness. She sounded almost as wholesome as ten pounds of stewed spinach. He could only hope for the best, considering all the trouble she was costing him. Muggsy said that Alice was sophisticated, but Muggsy wouldn't know; the nearest Muggsy ever had come to kissing a girl was making a grab for one, missing her in his myopia, and bumping his nose against a telephone pole. Muggsy was some Romeo!

Not that Jeremy could truthfully call himself much better. Alice was the fourth girl he had taken to a dance in three years of college. The first had been Betsy Pringle—another of Muggsy's mother's selections. Betsy had sung in his ear all the time she had been dancing; she had driven him almost crazy. He guessed that he could have kissed her good night, but he hadn't wanted to; she might have burst into Brunehilde's war song from *Die Walküre*. Duncan Faust had arranged for him his second date with a girl in town named Mildred Hawes. She had been a striking brunette, tall, shapely, graceful. Most fellows thought Mildred was pretty, a few called her beautiful, but Jeremy also thought that she was dumb. Through four hours of a Barbarian football dance she had not spoken more than sixteen words: "Isn't it hot? . . . Let's sit this one out . . . Gee, I'd like to dance with that cutie!" Jeremy had let her dance with all the cuties he could find for her, but underneath he had been hurt, sensing that Mildred wouldn't have come with him if there had been anyone else to take her to the dance. He had been resentful and unhappy all through the evening, and when he had taken her home the girl had teased him. "You're the moody one, you are. I bet there are dark thoughts going on behind that terrible frown you're wearing."

Jeremy had supposed he was acting like a bad sport, and, anyhow, here on the dark street he had had no need to share Mildred with anyone. She hadn't seemed to mind his arm around her waist; and when his heart had begun to beat faster at her closeness, she had appeared to understand for she had stopped and waited for him to gather up his courage. His kiss had been awkward and boyish, but Mildred, holding her mouth up against his own, had given him a lesson in experience.

"There, you're acting like a better boy."

Jeremy had kissed her again, excited by her nearness, remembering the girls Patsy DiOrio and Toady Reed talked about.

"My, but you're the rough one," Mildred had said, breaking away. "I must say, you're the strange boy all right. The jumps are in your arms, but not in your legs. You're an ice box at a dance, but on a dark street . . ."

Jeremy had stepped away from her, almost as though by reflex action. Then she had noticed his affliction and had held it against him. He hadn't been able to walk her home fast enough after that.

Jeremy could almost smile now, remembering Mildred. He could smile likewise over Gwen, his cousin whom mom had insisted he take to one of the college dances. Gwen had come down for the sophomore hop, mom had paid for the subscription, and Jeremy had arranged his program so that he had only danced once with Gwen. He had had a wonderful time, and for next to nothing, whereas poor old Gwen had been forced to dance three numbers with Muggsy, who had stepped on the same corn every waltz. Betsy, Mildred, Gwen —and now Alice. Jeremy reached the brightly lighted downtown shopping section with his spirits lifting. Luckily he found a haberdasher who hadn't closed his shop.

"A dollar and a half for that tie!" Jeremy wanted to wring the fellow's neck with it. "It's robbery and you know it!"

"Come back tomorrow morning and I'll let you have it for seventy-five cents," the shopkeeper said blandly.

Jeremy paid the dollar and a half. Going back across the campus, he fell to humming "My Sweet Little Alice Blue Gown."

III

Alice and Flo had retreated to the powder room, ostensibly to rescue their hair-dos, although Jeremy suspected that it was more likely they wanted a chance to rest their weary feet. Leaning against the doorway to the gym, Jeremy listened to the music and watched the dancers. The clock above the swimming pool said it was five minutes to two; in an hour the junior prom would be no more than a memory for another year. Jeremy was sad to think of that, for he had had a good time. Alice had proved to be one of the nicest girls Jeremy ever had known—unaffected, a good sport, a pleasant conversationalist. Dancing with her had been strangely exhilarating; her hair possessed a clean, sweet scent; her cheek, resting softly against his own, had made him want the waltzes to go on forever. Jeremy had to confess that for once Muggsy's mother had been a fine picker. He was going to ask Alice to the military ball.

Muggsy said, "They're taking a long time. I promised this next dance to Iron Man. I wish they'd hurry."

"The way you've been trampling poor Flo's feet, I wouldn't blame her if she never showed up."

The music stopped. Jeremy watched the couples strolling from the floor. The girls looked pretty in their long dresses and their corsages; and the men had that flushed appearance that came after four or five hours in a tuxedo. Around the walls were a series of booths where the couples sat between dances; there were comfortable chairs and candy and the inevitable chaperones. The chatter of voices and the laughter were nice to hear; Jeremy ignored Muggsy's impatient striding before the doorway and smiled. The decorations for the dance were really fine; evergreens banked around the walls, little rustic fences dividing the booths, colored lights burning under the water in the swimming pool. The soph hop had been a bit too garish with that Old Mexico motif, and the football dance too plain with goal posts and stuffed dummies of football players. But the prom was something special, and Jeremy regretted sorely that the end was now so near. Muggsy emitted a relieved sigh; the girls were coming back. The music began again, a waltz. Jeremy reached out his hand to Alice.

"I'm sorry we were so long, Jeremy."

"I didn't mind."

"Flo had a run in her stocking. She was practically in tears, but the matron mended it."

His arm around her slim shoulders gave him a wonderful sense of manliness. She danced well, not at all stiff and bossy like Flo. And her cheek, resting first on his shoulder and then against his own cheek as she looked up and smiled, filled his head with romantic fancies. He had a fleeting glimpse of Lizzie Whitman, stiff and immaculate, playing bridge with three other chaperones; of Twissy puffing drowsily on a big black cigar; of the dean of men sorting through a box of candy with a deepening frown, apparently put out by the fact that his favorite pieces were eaten. But Jeremy's reveries did not dwell long on the dean or Lizzie or Twissy; tonight belonged to soft music and dim lights, to the scent of gardenias and the rustle of silks and taffeta, to small, intimate talk, to laughter, to a feeling of chivalry and high fun, to cutting in and cutting back—and most of all to Alice. Perhaps he was falling in love—a lot of guys fell in love prom week end. In another year—at his last college prom—Jeremy was to know the answer to the question in his mind.

By then he had found the right girl.

IV

"Aw, Muggsy," Jeremy said, "I wish you'd stop living in the past. The prom's been over for a month."

"I've waited two weeks for a letter from Flo," Muggsy wailed. "She's through with me. It's all because of that movie we went to before the house parties. I didn't have any sense. I thought wearing glasses made me look funny so I took them off. We sit in the fourth row and can I see the picture? No! Flo says, 'Who's that playing the part of the butler?' I can't see, so I say, 'Eric Blore.' Flo looks at me kind of queer; he's not even in the picture, but how would I know? A little later Flo says, 'Don't you think that old lady ought to sit down; she's been standing there for almost a minute.' I laugh. 'Maybe she likes to stand,' I say. Flo gets angry. 'She doesn't like to stand, you idiot. She's waiting for you to stand up so she can get by.' My gosh, how could I see? So I jump up, and knock off the poor old thing's hat, and hit a girl in the stomach diving to find it (the hat, of course, not the stomach), and I can't find it but just keep pawing over everybody's feet, and all the time my glasses are in my pocket but I won't take 'em out, figuring I'm in this thing too deep by then, and—" Muggsy broke off with a groan; his romances were a succession of miserable anticlimacteries.

Jeremy grinned. Muggsy would never have any sense where girls were concerned, and if he lived to be hundred and ten he would still go on acting like a character in a Booth Tarkington story. More than anything in the world Muggsy wanted to kiss a girl, and still hadn't. Muggsy was like a good wool blanket—100 per cent virgin. But Muggsy had his virtues. More than anyone Jeremy knew, Muggsy was a clean talker about girls.

Muggsy's innocence toward girls (whom, of course, he called women) was not strictly atypical. Compared to Patsy DiOrio, to Toady Reed, or to Visch, Muggsy was painfully adolescent. In Patsy's opinion, and in Toady's, Muggsy was simply a sap, but Visch took a more charitable view: Muggsy was badly educated on matters relating to sex. Certainly there was no need for him to remain so; a bull session that did not eventually evolve into a spirited and intimate discussion of sex somehow failed to fulfill its historic mission. But sex consciousness was a normal part of growing up; it was natural and decent if one were permitted to accept it in that spirit. It wasn't because Muggsy and Jeremy were in college that they talked about sex; if they hadn't been in college they would have talked about sex on a street corner or wherever a group of growing boys congregated.

Even in Jeremy's generation—the so-called enlightened generation—sex education was neglected. Mostly what a bull session was endeavoring to supply was the truth about a really simple force of nature, and yet for some strange reason adults were hesitant to understand that fact, and so beclouded the subject with a silly atmosphere of mystery that filled an adolescent's mind with half truths and stirred up intense and perverted curiosities. Nature accepted sex as logical and respectable; it was only people—unhappily misinformed, in the main—who lost the gift of simplicity and directness in dealing with sex and so left a youngster in doubt, more or less defying him to find out what he could, and forcing the whole issue undercover where it became tainted with smuttiness and an air of exaggerated excitement.

The first round of Barbarian smokers, when the university physician spoke, clarified many misconceptions in Jeremy's mind. There wasn't any mystery whatever. People mated and babies were born. If sex were all that was at the bottom of their union, they simply had the babies. If love were the real motivating force, then they had the babies because they wanted them. They were happy in their babies and happy in their love, and that was practically the whole of the matter.

The university physician could see Toady Reed's cynical smile; Toady was the great disbeliever about everything.

"You think it's all a matter of chemistry, Toady?"

"Isn't it?"

The university physician leaned over and tapped Toady's head. "About ninety per cent of it is up here. Sex is much more a part of your mental life than your physical life; as far as getting it started, anyhow. Loose talk breeds loose thinking, Toady; it's dangerous."

Toady was beginning to blush. "Love isn't the only base to sex, sir."

"The only good base. But love isn't a definitive term, Toady. If you haven't the intelligence for complete love, you'll have to get along with part love, and that's too bad. But that's the real point of education, Toady: human relationships—a man's ability to live with his fellow men. Basically education is good or bad in the degree in which it serves a man in his life with the people he cares for. Happiness, success, a man's inner fulfillment all share one thing in common with charity. They begin at home: a man, a woman, their children."

"I suppose you object to kissing, sir!" Toady's voice was a little spiteful.

The university physician chuckled. "It's unsanitary, but then at times so is breathing. You'll have to let your conscience be your guide, Toady; once again, your education will determine your tastes."

Coming home after kissing Mildred Hawes good night, Jeremy was to remember the university physician's advice and to understand its wisdom more fully. Even in matters of the heart experience was a provocative teacher, one of the best. But books played their part. It was rumored that the university library possessed an excellent collection of erotica, but Jeremy, through all of his browsing among the book-stacks, never found it; if the books existed they were prudently kept under lock and key, and Jeremy, who was certainly no prude, admitted that there was sound reason for so doing. On the other hand, there were more than enough of risque reading available through other channels. Boston had merely to ban a book to guarantee that everyone in Hegeman or Spook's Hole would read it; intellectual independence was given as the excuse, but that was eyewash. A curiosity to see how naughty the book might be was at the base of its popularity; the Boston censors rarely disappointed their reading public. An unexpurgated *Lady Chatterly's Lover* or *Studs Lonigan* were examples of books that passed from hand to hand; Jeremy read them all, but his good sense told him not to brood over them.

"The stuff makes me sick," Muggsy said. "Sure, it's realism, of a sort; but I don't want to be like that, Jeremy. I don't even want to think like that."

Jeremy grinned, more at himself than at Muggsy. In the end he couldn't escape his home training. For all the talk about girls and sex, for all the books that were so outspoken, there was a line over which he couldn't step. Sometimes he resented the fact that mom and pop had told him so little, but in the thing that counted most they had not sent him to college untutored. He never once had doubted the love between mom and pop. Their love had proved an anchor, a symbol of steadfastness. Perhaps a Toady Reed or a Patsy DiOrio were without this support. Perhaps any undergraduate who talked and acted like a sap over girls and sex was only trying to cover up an instability within himself that had its source in his own home. Jeremy could reason that this explanation might not be all-inclusive in every case, but he was sure that where love was steadfast at home it was easier to keep one's sense of moral equilibrium. As the university physician had said, love was the only real and dependable base. Love was the experience you sought. If you could keep your mind clean, then you could keep your heart clean, and your love would be richer.

"You talk like Beatrice Fairfax," Muggsy said disgustedly. "You'll end up running a lonely hearts club."

Jeremy smiled. Muggsy hadn't yet met Agnes Walling. Jeremy himself had only met her once, and then for an hour.

V

Agnes was a senior at the College for Women. She was standing on the steps of the library, talking to Duncan Faust, when Jeremy came out into the chill drizzle of a late October afternoon. She wore a light tan raincoat that made her seem small and fragile against the tall old trees and the great dome of dark, overcast sky. Her face was uplifted and Jeremy noticed the short, round little nose that turned up at the end, the chin that gave a hint of quiet, unshakable determination. A wisp of brownish-blonde hair had escaped the brim of her hat, and she pushed it back with annoyance. But it was her eyes that Jeremy really liked. They were grayish blue, eyes that were filled with fun and friendliness and common sense. This girl, Jeremy thought, was no Mildred Hawes; something about Agnes Walling—perhaps her warm, quick smile, perhaps her complete naturalness of manner as she stood now with her hands in the pockets of her coat and a notebook under her arm—told him that this girl was real.

"We've been talking about you," Duncan said. "Agnes liked the editorial you wrote in *Targum* about Sunday chapel and the old woman who clutched the crucifix."

Jeremy's heart was warm. "Why did you like it?"

"It seemed honest."

"I was telling her about the sandwich route and how you threw it up after Robert Hare's death," Duncan said.

"It seemed dumb just letting college breeze by like that."

The girl laughed. "You're not dumb."

"But broke. I had to borrow four hundred dollars from my brother-in-law to come back to school my senior year. I hope he gets it back some day."

"He will," the girl said.

"Why are you so sure?"

"Because of you. You're honest. And, to be perfectly honest now, I've got to be getting back to Cooper Hall for supper."

"Can I come with you?"

"You'll have to run."

"We'll make it in fifteen minutes."

"We'd better if I don't want to starve."

Agnes kept her hands in her pockets, the notebook pressed against her side, her head bent down against the rain. Jeremy, striding up the campus pathway by her side, was happy. He said impulsively, "I like you, Agnes."

"Then take my arm and help me over this puddle," Agnes said practically.

Jeremy began to hope that he had found his girl.

He saw Agnes on Wednesday and again on Friday, and on Saturday they went to a dance at the College of Agriculture given by the Horticulture Club.

Jeremy waited in the sitting room of Jameson Dormitory, feeling conspicuous when a girl in a faded bathrobe, her hair in curlers, clomped down the hall in a pair of bedroom slippers. But the girl ignored him eloquently; he wasn't her date. Another girl came into the room, took up her knitting, then fled when she noticed him. Jeremy was beginning to wonder if he had the measles, but Agnes laughed at his perturbation.

"They know you're my property tonight, Jeremy. Do you mind?"

He shook his head, earnestly.

"You'll have to take my hand," Agnes said. "I know it's false pride, but I won't wear my glasses—not to our first dance."

Jeremy wanted to tease her, but he was pleased, too. The night was cold, but dry and clear. The walk across the College of Agriculture campus raised his spirits and bolstered his courage. By the pond where the willow trees hung over the water he stopped and turned.

"I want to kiss you, Agnes."

"Part of routine, Jeremy?"

Suddenly he was deeply jealous. There must have been other dances, other fellows. He kissed her without answering, then walked on, still sullen. But before they reached the building where the dance was being held, he told her the truth. "I've never gone with many girls, Agnes."

The pressure of her fingers tightened against his hand.

"It wasn't routine," he blurted, halfway up the steps.

Agnes said nothing, but she thought that any girl would have known. Beyond the door the orchestra began to play.

Back in Hegeman, a week later, Muggsy said ominously, "Boy, you're on the hook!"

"Meaning what?"

"You know what I mean. Nobody sees you any more."

Jeremy scowled. He knew well enough to whom Muggsy had been talking. His mother. And of course Mrs. Lippincott didn't want Muggsy becoming entangled with a steady girl. Jeremy was angry that Muggsy and his mother couldn't mind their own affairs, but a sense of guilt plagued him nonetheless. His own father and mother had sacrificed for his education. Although they had never said so, Jeremy felt that they expected him to repay them after college. Becoming involved with Agnes wasn't going to be to their liking, either. He shook his head, rebellious. That problem would have to work itself out.

All through college he had wanted a girl, and now that he had found one he wasn't going to become a monk merely to satisfy Muggsy or his mother. Agnes filled all his thoughts; she was in his mind when he was studying, and nights when he carried his editorials down to *Targum,* and in class when a lecture was dull. He remembered the richness of her voice, and smiled to himself when he thought how she hadn't wanted to wear her glasses to their first dance; and in his mind there was always that picture of the first time they had met: the girl in the tan raincoat, the rain on her face, the notebook under her arm. He felt at ease with her; her friendship wore well. All the social estrangement that had dogged his adolescence and had hurt so deeply when the fraternities had passed him by no longer mattered when he was with Agnes. She gave him a sense of walking on firm ground, for she accepted him as he was. How could Muggsy understand that? Or even mom and pop? Agnes was a reality he had stumbled upon in the cold drizzle of an October day; he had possessed the good judgment to know it, and he was pleased with his own good intelligence.

Within a month Jeremy was seeing Agnes all the time, and the College for Women campus was becoming almost as familiar as his own. He came to know the other girls in Agnes's dormitory: Jean, Miriam, Edith, Lois. He shared their secrets. Edith had an electric percolator that she hid in her trunk; making coffee in dormitory rooms instead of going over to Cooper Hall for breakfast was against rules, but Edith brewed it every Saturday morning and Miriam stood by the door fanning away the fumes so that the house mother wouldn't be warned. There was a book in which the girls had to sign going on, and coming from, a date, but sometimes when they were late their roommates signed for them. The almost complete freedom of life on the campuses of the col-

leges for men was not shared at the College for Women; restrictions were imposed in countless little ways—limited areas
for smoking; set hours when the girls could entertain their
friends, especially in the basement lounge room; strict ac-
countability as to who the chaperones would be on engage-
ments off the campus. Jeremy chafed under the rules and
regulations that now touched his existence so intimately.

"They simply don't trust anybody," he ranted, never over-
gracious when he encountered some new taboo.

But Agnes only laughed. "We're the gentle sex. We have
to be sheltered."

"That's rubbish. Miriam could outbox me and Edith
could run the legs off me, and you know it!"

"Then perhaps you're being protected," Agnes said, giving
a turn to the matter that didn't altogether please him.

If he needed protection from anyone, Jeremy thought, it
was from Miss Sprig, the house mother of Jameson. Miss
Sprig was a wiry little spinster who quite obviously preferred
to think of herself as a "maiden lady"; she was clearly ill at
ease in the company of men and looked upon them all with
suspicion regardless of their age, for even small boys were not
above scribbling naughty words on sidewalks; she gave the
impression that she disguised herself as a mouse, eaves-
dropped at bull sessions in Hegeman and Spook's Hole, and
believed every wild statement uttered. Expecting trouble
from this source sooner or later, Jeremy was not surprised
when Agnes informed him one afternoon, "Miss Sprig had
me in her room for almost an hour last night. She thinks that
we're seeing too much of each other, and that it's bad for
us—bad for our studies and for us as persons."

"Miss Sprig belongs in a convent."

"She was terribly distraught, Jeremy. She said there had
been talk about us, we had been seen together so much. She
thinks it's bad for the reputation of the college."

Jeremy could see that Agnes's pride had been hurt by the

interview with Miss Sprig; his anger was deeper for that reason. A college for women, he supposed, had to set barriers around itself—for want of a better phrase, to be prudent and cautious—but when its suspicions were unfounded, they seemed ridiculous and just a trifle perverted, as though like some wayward small boy all the naughty words were stored away in its mind and never found release in sidewalk scribbling.

"Do you want to see less of me, Agnes?"

"Of course not. But Miss Sprig—"

"Miss Sprig be hanged," Jeremy said indignantly. "She'll either have to grow up to us or go into her convent!"

He did not have to walk the mile and a half back to Hegeman alone. In the afternoons there was always someone from the College of Agriculture going back to the main campus, in the evenings some other student from the men's colleges who was manifesting faithfulness in his attentions at the College for Women. There were perhaps a dozen in this latter group, and no small spirit of fraternity existed between them; Jeremy's companion that afternoon was a classmate named Johnny Leeds, a major in engineering who was older than most undergraduates, a chap already in his early thirties who smoked a pipe and took every problem of life with earnestness.

"Miss Sprig?" asked Johnny, who smelled of after shave lotion. "It's up in her mind, as you say, but then she's probably afraid of her job if there's too much talk."

"There's nothing wrong in seeing your girl, Johnny."

"It's an old custom, heaven knows. Some universities have special dormitories for students who are married, and that makes a lot of sense in cases where a chap is mature in his outlook and tastes. Over here, of course, if a gal gets married she has to get out of the dormitories, although I can understand that. Married people are more uninhibited toward life, and they ought to stick together."

"You mean that's what is on Miss Sprig's mind? That she thinks we're becoming a borderline case?"

"Well, aren't you? After all, they have twelve hundred unmarried gals on their hands over here. They have to be alert."

"Do they do the proposing for you at the right moment?"

Johnny Leeds said one of the rare humorous remarks of his life. "In her lower desk drawer the dean keeps a little golden shotgun for guys like us."

But Jeremy didn't even smile. "How do you know when you're in love, Johnny?"

The engineer sucked on his pipe, disconcerted. "Hell, Jeremy, that's a funny question. You're still a kid all right. Why don't you ask Miss Sprig? No," Johnny said, taking himself with deep seriousness, "don't do that. Maybe she loved and lost, and I don't think that's a good point of view. Or maybe she couldn't ever get out of herself long enough to fall in love, and that's no good, either. Damn, Jeremy, I don't know what to say; I'm an engineer and not a philosopher. If you want to live for somebody else, if their happiness comes first in your calculations, I guess you're in love. But it's an amateur's opinion."

Now Jeremy could smile. Johnny Leeds had been trained to the scientific approach; every statement had to be tested and proved and the observable result set down; all of his thinking processes were colored, even in matters relating to the heart.

"On the other hand," Johnny said, "you can fall in love with love. That happens a lot among guys your age, Jeremy. The thought of being in love is pleasing to the ego; it gives you a sense of social security. Girls get bitten by that bug more than fellows, but nature is on their side. Marriage is mighty important to a gal, and sometimes even a bad marriage seems more important than none at all. I've seen cases like that. Again, it's the old ego becoming overinvolved, and that's the fastest way to get a bad marriage. You've got to get outside of yourself to know it's love. Or did I say that once?"

"You did."

"Then I've said what I had to say," retorted Johnny, a scientist to the end.

They reached the main campus and Johnny went on to the library, Jeremy to supper in the cafeteria in Winants. Jeremy knew that he had no business thinking of marriage —not without even the prospect of a job. He wanted to be level-headed and fair. Some day he wanted to be married, to have kids. He wanted to be married to Agnes. It was funny how when you came to college you wanted to conquer the world, and believed that maybe you could. Secretly you thought of yourself as some day being famous and probably well-to-do, if not actually wealthy, and getting ahead in the world seemed more important than anything. But education played tricks with your sense of values. You came to under- stand that a Twissy or a Dickie Morris probably never had made more than four or five thousand dollars a year, and yet they were happy in what they were doing. That was what education should teach you: to live to be happy within your- self. If a girl like Agnes meant that happiness, then your edu- cation should lead you to an Agnes. Your education and her education had given you a base on which to build a vital life —a life in terms of home and love and children. Jeremy went on to his supper, content in his reasoning.

But Miss Sprig's talk with Agnes had one effect; Jeremy no longer felt at ease spending his afternoons at Jameson, and he began meeting Agnes downtown. Sometimes they simply walked around the campus, but some days were too cold or wet for that. Sometimes they went to Louie's for a milk shake and spent the afternoon in a booth, watching those who came in and talking about classes and Miss Sprig and how poorly the college was organized for a couple who wanted to go steady. Agnes was a major in psychology; Jeremy had studied introductory psychology in his sophomore year, and he remembered those long afternoon labs, the experiments with tuning forks to prove there were sounds the human ear could not hear, the sets of numbers that were flashed before your eyes to test your powers of memory and recall, and Muggsy's unprofitable conflict with the scientific method when he tried to inject a sense of humor into his lab reports. (Muggsy had written, explaining his own weakness at recalling sets of unrelated digits, "It must be organic; I always remember blondes by their faces and not their telephone numbers," and had received a flat zero for his effort.) But Agnes was more annoyed than amused at Muggsy; she liked her major, and while psychology might be a young science, she didn't want Jeremy to laugh at it even through the guise of an anecdote involving Muggsy.

"What's so sacred about psychology?"

"Nothing has to be sacred if you want to be dumb about it. It doesn't hurt a man to admit he doesn't know everything perfectly; and you just do have a smattering on that subject, Jeremy."

Underneath he admitted it was so, but he was irked at her criticism. He sulked and Agnes let him. A day later the tension was past, but not the feeling of awkwardness. Another cold, unpleasant day—and Louie's again. Actually they both sensed that they were out of step with college routine, that they probably were being silly and stubborn, but there was an added reason for being together, if it were only to worry Miss Sprig a little more. And then Silvers came over to Miss Sprig's side.

"How about your studies, Jeremy?"

"They're fine."

"You're giving this girl an awful lot of time. You're acting pretty serious."

"Is that wrong, sir?"

"It depends on how serious you mean to be. You have to be fair about this, Jeremy, or else one of you is going to be hurt and hurt deeply."

"You mean my affliction, sir?"

"Not at all. I mean that you've never gone much with girls, and perhaps Agnes hasn't gone much with boys. You may both be lonely for the experience of going with someone. That's puppy love, and it shouldn't be taken too seriously. I'd hate to see you get so far off the track that you smashed up in your senior year. You ought to think this thing through, Jeremy."

"What if I have, sir?"

"Have you?"

Jeremy shook his head. He hadn't thought it through—not completely. Somehow it wasn't necessary to think. He merely accepted being with Agnes as part of his day.

"Perhaps it is real, then," Silvers said. "To you, Jeremy. I hope it's real with Agnes, too. That would be fine. Love is the acid test of how grown up you can be intellectually and emotionally—grown up in terms of being honest. Please think it through, boy; I want you to find happiness as much as though you were my own son."

Jeremy lost any feeling of resentment. Meeting Agnes that day on the steps of the library had brought him unexpected problems. For the first time he was a trifle worried.

VI

Howard Blakely was a member of Alpha Chi Rho who took a course with Twissy. Jeremy scarcely knew his name; Howard was a thin, gaunt boy in faded slacks who sat in the last row and seldom recited. If Howard had cut class for a month, Jeremy never would have noticed; he simply never thought of Howard. But one day after class the Alpha Chi said, "I've seen you around with Agnes Walling."

"Do you know her?" Jeremy asked.

"I took Agnes to a house party once. Remember me to her."

Jeremy walked away stiffly, consumed with jealousy. In retrospect even Howard's tone of voice seemed to taunt him as though there were shadowy implications behind his remarks. Jeremy knew that it would be better if he forgot the entire incident, but the demon of his jealousy stalked through his mind. He had heard fellows talk in bull sessions about girls; he knew what they said about hot neckers and petters. Suddenly his heart was heavy with distrust, and he despised himself for that also, for he was judging Agnes simply because he had listened to Patsy DiOrio or Toady Reed. His sullen mood grew on him despite his feeling of pettiness and unfairness; after all, what right had he to think it was any worse for Agnes to go with Howard Blakely than it had been for him to go with Mildred Hawes? But Mildred was the type of girl who was talked about . . . No, he told himself angrily, that was being cheap and suspicious and unreasonable. He had to forget about Howard. But he couldn't; over a milk shake at Louie's the question came out before he could catch himself.

"Why didn't you tell me about Howard?"

Agnes said, "What was there to tell you?"

"At least that you knew him."

Agnes reached out and took his hand. "Jeremy," she said, "you're being unkind. You've had to grow up and so have I."

He looked down his nose, ashamed. "Let's not mention it again."

"No," Agnes said, "let's be honest about the whole thing. My mother and father are wonderful people, Jeremy; church people who never drink or swear or run around. They've raised three children—that and supporting their church has been their life. When I came to college, I didn't know anything about boys except what I heard and read; but I didn't want to be a wallflower all my life, either—no girl does. And so when my roommate got me a date with Howard I went, for I was sick of just being in college to study and never having any fun. It was a dull dance, Jeremy; the boys were dull, I thought, but I blamed myself. Maybe I didn't know how to have fun. There was a girl there named Mildred Hawes who seemed to be having a wonderful time. I ran into her once on the porch being kissed by one boy and again in the hall being kissed by another. That second time she put her head on the boy's shoulder, looked me straight in the eye, and winked. I've never forgotten it.

"Later I went downtown with Howard for something to eat. He was trying awfully hard to be nice. When we drove back to the fraternity he parked the car and put his arm around me. He was all right at first; he talked and kissed me and talked some more. But the things he said were getting suggestive; I could feel myself tightening up inside; I couldn't trust him. Remember, Jeremy, I was only a kid, a lonesome kid, growing up as every girl has to. I didn't want to be another Mildred Hawes, that was all; Howard grew bolder and I just pushed. Harder than I meant to, I guess; he landed on the floor. He was terribly mad and I didn't blame him. Without a word he started the car and drove me back to Jameson. He even forgot to say good night."

Jeremy almost chuckled. "You bet he was mad."

"I didn't care."

"But you helped him to grow up, too."

Agnes said, "I never thought of that."

Jeremy said, looking down at the table, "I once went to a dance with Mildred Hawes."

Agnes tried to sound indifferent. "Did you enjoy it?"

"What do you think?"

"That you probably had the same impulses as Howard Blakely."

"Not with Mildred," Jeremy said. "I'm not the kind of fellow Mildred wants."

Louie came and took away the empty milk shakes; it was almost time for Agnes to walk back to supper in Cooper Hall.

"See you tomorrow?"

"I've got to study for a quiz in sociology."

"We can study together."

"Do you think it will work?"

How would they know unless they tried? When he left Agnes at Cooper he looked around, hoping to find Johnny Leeds, but he was too late for Johnny. He walked back alone, thinking about Howard and what Johnny had said about love and marriage and about Agnes.

Studying for the quiz in sociology was the worst kind of bore. The course was sound enough, the subject matter admittedly vital, but the textbook was as poorly written as any over which Jeremy ever had agonized. He had suffered the same sad experience his sophomore year in studying economics, and in his junior year in international law. The authors of college textbooks were simply an inarticulate lot; they wrote dully and too often aimlessly; they lost the correlation between life and knowledge and became involved in their own sterile impreachments. Sociology appeared to be the classic example of them all, and that was nonsensical, for here was a subject about people and yet the pulsebeat of humanity had been permitted to become stilled. The whole thing was a chore when it had no need to be; Agnes was as relieved as he when the task was completed.

"Psychology is more fun, Jeremy. At least that seems real enough to be applied to your own life. Take the encouraging data we studied today. There are fewer divorces among college graduates as a group than any other."

"And fewer babies."

"Of course there are, but that makes sense, too. Having children is a serious responsibility; you want to play fair with youngsters. Marriage is serious, too; you want to give it a chance to last. College people do, anyhow, if you can trust statistics. I guess it's simply the fact that education broadens your point of view, toward people as well as toward things, and you are better able to appreciate true values. Mainly it's the early years of marriage that are difficult; you don't have too much money, you can't go around a great deal or entertain, and then if the babies come along early they tie you down. If two people can't live alone, discovering their happiness in themselves and in simple, everyday experiences, they soon find it out."

Jeremy sat on a table in the lounge room of Jameson, his arms around his knees. He had been thinking seriously of marriage lately, but it seemed that for the most part his mind had been building barriers against it. He had obligations about which to think before marriage: getting a start in his own professional career, helping out mom and pop, paying back the money he had borrowed to finish his college education. But looking down at Agnes, seeing the deep earnestness in her eyes, the gentleness of her lips, he knew that it was mostly himself he distrusted. He would never understand why a girl like Agnes was willing to risk her future with a man who could only offer her vague promises that he might make his way in the world. It seemed a wild, a foolish gamble. Even love wasn't enough. You had to eat. You had to pay rent. And yet, he admitted, the thought of the risk was exciting, a high adventure. There was a tremendous heartlift in thinking that you could do it, that the two of you could stand against the world and practically defy the laws of gravitation. Just for an instant he wanted to ask Agnes. Would she marry him?

And then another door opened in his heart and he faced the real reason for his hesitancy. His affliction. It was always there somehow; he had no wish to overdramatize it, but there it remained nonetheless. His affliction set him apart. It made problems for him that he still felt he had no right to ask anyone else to share—unless they knew. He looked at his watch and was glad it was almost time to go. His moodiness, coming upon him all at once as a mist will rise from a meadow in early spring, was obvious. His quick sense of unhappiness, his dejected spirit, his feeling that the ivy years in the end weren't going to make a great deal of difference were emotions he couldn't very well disguise.

Agnes said, "You look tired."

"I am." But when he left her he wanted to turn back. At least he would play fair with Agnes. Unless he could have the honesty to wait now until she knew, he could never trust his heart against his emotions. But he was afraid, more afraid than he ever had been in all his life.

The situation reached a crisis within a week. Agnes asked Jeremy to the Christmas dance at the College for Women, and on the Sunday afternoon before, Jeremy came over to hear the Christmas music in the chapel. The place was crowded when they arrived, and Jeremy could not sit on the end of the aisle where he preferred and always felt more at ease, but was forced to sit toward the center of the aisle where he could only feel squeezed in and uncomfortable. The carols were beautifully sung, but Jeremy couldn't enjoy them. The closeness of the other people made him conscious principally that he was overtired, and his nerves were jumpy. He tried all the tricks he relied on in strange environments when these nervous spells seized him. He wiped his nose. He closed his eyes and tried to think of the color blue—one blue circle after another stretching on and on. He held a hymnal in his hand, clutching it, straining to control the tremors that increased with his growing uneasiness. But none of the old ruses would work. He was conscious in the end only of the fact that he was becoming conspicuous, that very likely he was annoying everyone around him. His cheeks began to burn with the shame of his weakness. At least, he thought, Agnes could see for once just how treacherously his affliction betrayed him when he fought against it the hardest. It was no use. He couldn't sit there any longer, an eyesore, a disturbance. At the end of the number he rose and walked stiffly down the aisle. His face was red.

He had said nothing to Agnes; he hoped that she would stay for the remainder of the music. He didn't want sympathy, and least of all pity. This was his problem and he had to see it through alone. He didn't expect anyone to understand. He was simply put together that way, and he had to like it.

Outside the chapel the cold air struck him with a clean, harsh chillness that was wonderfully invigorating. He stood, breathing deeply, and thinking: "I'm a different person out here. I can't explain it to anyone."

A hand touched his arm. He turned quickly. But Agnes asked for no explanation. She smiled, a bright, determined smile, and then she took his cheeks in her mittened hands and kissed his lips.

"I love you, Jeremy," she said.

He held her close, suddenly happy, wondering with an almost malicious enjoyment if this were against Miss Sprig's sense of propriety.

"I'm awfully hungry, Jeremy. Could we go downtown and have dinner together?"

"If you like."

"I'd like very much to see us always stand together."

Jeremy took her arm and they went along the icy campus pathway.

"It doesn't matter, Agnes?"

"Why should it? You're more than nerves, Jeremy. You're head and heart and soul and love. We'll make a go of it. We've got something to hold onto. Call it faith or love or intelligence. It's all the same."

Jeremy saw the sun through the naked branches of the trees. The whole earth became bright and clean and warm. He stopped thinking of himself as a boy.

THE HOURS OF DECISION

I

Spring on the campus was the golden season of the year. The old board running track behind the Engineering Building was taken up, and the candidates for the track team, who had looked numb with cold at practice through the blustery, uncertain weather of March, now moved to the cinder paths on Neilson Field. Lacrosse sticks bloomed almost as profusely as forsythia around the Chemistry Building, and baseball gloves and tennis racquets became familiar articles; with the warming sun and the lengthening days the crew went out on the Raritan River, the students in ROTC drilled more diligently for exhibition day in May, the lawn mowers were constantly buzzing over the campus grass; and as the sap began to run down the trunks of the cherry trees at the College Farm, the entire university seemed to rouse itself from its long winter slumber. Spring was better even than fall, despite the autumnal heartlift of coming back to school, of reviving old friendships and romanticizing the adventures of summer, of becoming submerged in another football season and wondering vaguely about the esoteric existence of the members of the cross country team as they chased off over hill and dale. Winter brought basketball, fencing, swimming, and wrestling, the sophomore hop and the junior prom, but winter also brought long, shut-in evenings, slush and sniffles and the grind of books. Spring was resurrection to nature and the male animal alike; ahead stretched final exams, alumni day, and commencement, but spring crept up on you with a seductive charm all its own, so that you thought of it only as a new beginning until you realized with something of a shock midway through May that it was also the ending.

But spring in the senior year, Jeremy discovered with a twinge of discomfiture, brought a new responsibility. Life had a disturbing habit of moving on. Now that the ivy years were all but ended, Jeremy might reasonably be consumed with nostalgia for the happy times that were almost gone forever; at the same time there was the future to face, and that meant finding a job. A senior simply could not escape this lingering worry; it was with him wherever he turned. Suddenly the ivy years appeared only an interruption in the old struggle for survival; Jeremy, facing the problem with uneasiness, felt as though Lizzie Whitman's favorite line from Browning had become a dark and ominous threat: "The last of life for which the first was made." The front page of *The Targum* began to feature a new type of news story. On Wednesday a representative from General Electric would be at the Office of Personnel and Placement to interview job candidates. On Friday the Standard Oil man would be on the campus. Next Tuesday the representative from International Business Machines. Jeremy read every notice, wondering uneasily who did hire the man who had majored in the liberal arts. All of the companies who sent agents to the campus seemed to be looking for engineers or chemists or research workers.

And yet as the weeks went by, a large number of seniors were finding jobs through the departments in which they had majored. The ceramists were placed, the aggies practically all in line for positions, the education majors faithfully finishing their practice teaching in fulfillment of the requirements for teaching permits, the pretheologs going on to Seminary, and the premedicals and the prelegals seeking graduate schools that would admit them. Duncan Faust, who had majored in business administration, had secured a position with a carloading company through the Office of Personnel and Placement and had celebrated that event by announcing his engagement to his home town girl. Johnny Leeds was going with General Electric and planned on being married in the chapel at the College for Women on the day after commencement.

"Everybody's thinking of tying a noose around his neck and getting set for life," growled Muggsy. "Not me. I'm going to be the eternal Peter Pan."

"Playing that lousy clarinet," said Jeremy, disgusted at the thought that Muggsy's musical accomplishments had not improved in four years. Muggsy didn't seem to have grown up at all, despite the fact that he did well in his classes; he was still principally the kid who had arrived in college with enough patent medicines to open an apothecary shop. He was still bound to his mother's apron strings; she picked his girls and made his decisions. In this respect Muggsy made Jeremy a little sick. But Dr. Will already had spoken to Muggsy about a job, whereas Will hadn't yet spoken to him, Jeremy reflected uncomfortably. Muggsy was set. But, Jeremy reasoned, Will had let him continue in journalism and therefore he would be getting his break one of these days.

At a Student Council meeting in the Beta House, Iron Man spoke about his own future. "When I came to college, I thought I was through with the old neighborhood, that I was going to be too good for it; but my old man wants me to come home and run his printing business and I'm going to. I've got ideas now; I think I can put new life in the old shop. It's funny how you think you'll never go back, and yet you do. I think that's most of what I've learned: it isn't where you are, but what you are that counts."

"You've had a good time at college," Jeremy said.

"A good time. Some day I'll be like the rest of the old guys who come back to the Beta House for reunions. I'll live in the past. But I have only one regret. If that big mug Dalmas would have come out onto Neilson Field and put on a uniform, I would have shown him who was going to get dumped on his fanny!"

"Robeson, too?"

Iron Man laughed. "Say, he's a great guy all right. I used to look down my nose at Niggers, but I'll never measure up to Robey. He could play football, too!"

Next morning there was a note in the mail box from Will, and Jeremy thought optimistically, "The old man's going to give me a break at last." He was at Will's office punctually at four.

The man was clearly unsettled. Jeremy sat down in a chair across from the desk, knowing what was coming. In his stomach he could feel the gnawing, uneasy hollowness caused by his disappointment and his discouragement, but outwardly he was calm and his wits collected. He was going to stand up to this thing. He wasn't going to let the old man think it made a particle of difference.

Will said, his manner agitated, "You remember the terms under which I permitted you to enroll in this course?"

Jeremy nodded. He looked at Will, feeling rather sorry for the man's flushed face and flustered expression. Poor old Visch had been forced to stand up to this thing twice at Columbia Dental School.

"I'm sorry, Baxter," Will said. "I simply can't recommend you for a job. You understand why?"

"Yes, sir. My physical condition. Shall I apologize for it, sir?"

Will's face reddened. "I have to stand by my standards, Baxter."

"I know that, sir."

"I've thought this through very carefully. I want to be fair

with you, but I've got to be fair with the department's reputation, too. This is a professional curriculum. It isn't you personally, but everyone in the curriculum who must be considered. If we say a man is ready for newspaper work, he must
be ready in every way. Our recommendation must mean that
in every case."

Jeremy's mouth tightened, but he forced a smile, a partially crooked smile. The old man was actually perspiring.
He was taking this duty badly, and the lines around his eyes
appeared deeper than Jeremy had remembered. "Is that all,
sir?"

"You shall graduate, of course."

"Thank you, sir."

"I wish you luck."

"I imagine I'll get along, sir."

The man stood up. He was visibly upset and his hand appeared to tremble as he held it out. As Jeremy clasped it, he
knew that he would never like Will, even though he understood the man's principles and rather respected his intellectual courage. As far as Will could see, the ivy years were
nearly over and they had made no difference in Jeremy's
case. But Jeremy could remember how he had stormed out of
the old man's office four years before, a distraught and heart-
broken boy. He wasn't doing that now. He was shaking Will's
hand. Then he was closing the door, quietly, conscious that
Will's glance followed him uncertainly. He went down the
stairs and out into the warm May sunshine. Well, that's that,
his mind seemed to say. But all the while the feeling of hollowness was growing. Growing and growing and growing.

II

At Landing Lane, a mile below Hegeman, there was a
bridge over the Raritan. When Jeremy reached there he
stopped, hooked his arms over the railing, and thought,
"This is rotten." Mom and pop were going to be terribly

angry when they heard about Will's decision; they were going to blame the college. Mom and pop had always coddled
him just a little; they had invented excuses when the breaks
went against him; perhaps that tendency made them mom
and pop. Now Jeremy understood that he had depended on
those excuses; they had made life extremely comfortable.
But old Will, and not mom and pop, recommended him for
a newspaper job. There wasn't any easy way around that fact.
This thing had to be presented to mom and pop so that they
would see it clearly and fairly. As Silvers had said once, there
was only one way you could deal with a bitter man and that
was to walk away from him.

Somehow just then Jeremy didn't want to think of Silvers;
underneath the man himself had the weakness of being a
coddler, especially toward those whom he liked. But Silvers
had been a wonderful influence in his life, a steadying hand,
a kind and tender voice. His counsel had been sound and
only a little stuffy, no small accomplishment for a pedagogue.
Still, in the end, the greatest lessons Silvers had taught him
had been by example rather than by preaching. That day,
four years ago, when he had stopped to change the battery in
his earphone, just as though nothing in the world could seem
more natural. Not forcing him to go back to *The Targum,*
but letting him think through the problem himself. Telling
him honestly that day of the N.Y.U. game that he had hurt
the coach by his story in the *Record.* More than anyone else
through all the ivy years Silvers had taught him that the man
counted first—what was in his heart even more than what was
in his head. Silvers would understand why he had held himself in before Will. It was the way Silvers himself would have
acted. If death took a son from you, you sought that boy in
others. You wore an earphone if you were partially deaf. You
shook hands when you met another man. Little things and
big things, some only surface deep and others rooted in the
very core of your character, and all together they constituted

the art of graceful living according to the code of a gentleman.

Agnes would be glad that he had held his tongue. Jeremy wondered how she was going to take this news. Standing up to it. Believing that he'd find a job sooner or later, a good job, a better job. Jeremy knew what she would say: "We can wait—ten years, if we have to." For a moment as Jeremy leaned upon the bridge railing and watched the radiating circles where the water flowed against the pilings, his heart was uncertain. He hadn't the prospect of a job, no printing business to go back to like Iron Man. In that respect he was no better off than when the ivy years had begun. But four years ago he hadn't been ready to meet Agnes. He had been all boy, bottled up inside himself, ready to whimper when life slapped him, empty-headed and easily swept away by his emotions. Somewhere along the way he had found at least the beginnings of self-discipline and objective reasoning. And of a firmer faith in God and himself and Agnes and others like Silvers and Twissy and Pete and Charlie the Bat. Somewhere along the way he had acquired the ability to see himself with almost honest detachment. He could not go on forever being an adolescent, either physically or intellectually, making himself the axis upon which the universe revolved. Happiness was strictly a relative term; it was something you found mostly outside yourself. In an Agnes. In friends. In the acts that were satisfying because they were right acts, honest acts. Jeremy thought with a smile that he was beginning to think like some self-sanctified old coot who had grown into a stuffed shirt. But he had begun to think more soberly, more seriously. About why people fell in love. About why they planned a life together. Naturally there was a physical attraction, but there had to be something more. Respect. Faith. Friendship.

Jeremy supposed that his wandering thoughts were getting far afield from the problem of old Will and where he was going to turn now to build his future, but all these thoughts were interrelated. His future, after all, depended on what he wanted from life. A home for Agnes. A home that was comfortable, where his friends could lounge around as they had in college—with a place to put their feet. A home with books —not books in fancy bindings, but books that were read and re-read and talked about, sometimes a bit extravagantly, for books were supposed to free your fancies. A home with a corner that belonged to him—a very messy corner probably, with a typewriter he usually forgot to cover, and papers scattered around, and old pipes in a bowl beside the dictionary. A home with kids in it—just average kids who left their playthings where you least expected them and so made you almost break your neck trying to step over them, kids who got a little dirty and went to Sunday School and had to be sent to bed early for being mischievous. Jeremy could see that home clearly in his mind; it was a home that Agnes and he had created one evening sitting on the steps of Jameson as the night watchman had gone from house to house testing the doors.

"I've dreamed about that home ever since I was a runny-nosed little girl in pigtails," Agnes had said.

Jeremy had followed the course of the night watchman, realizing sadly that it was time for him to go. "We'll have that home," he had promised. Of all the dreams that had filled the ivy years, this seemed the sweetest.

It still seemed so. But without a job there wasn't going to be any home. And just any old job wasn't the answer, either. A good part of a man's life went into his work. It should be work that a man enjoyed, that there was satisfaction in doing, and a sense of reward not measured entirely by the fatness of the pay envelope. The man who belonged in the home Agnes and he had planned must be a man who had found a solid contentment in life through performing work that appeared worth doing.

Jeremy sighed. It was a big order. And less than an hour ago Dr. Will had labelled him unemployable. But was he? Suppose he were applying to an employer for a position, what could he say in his own behalf? For one thing, he would tell him truthfully about his affliction, acknowledging its limiting factors, and not embarrass the man in the telling but let him see that it was just one of those things, like Silvers changing the battery in his earphone. He would tell him about Visch watching him as he slept, keeping count of the tremors, performing a kind, unselfish service of friendship. He would tell him how Billy Farrand had ridden him on *The Targum* in the hope that he could beat the system that Billy hadn't, and he would tell him about the Barbarians and how he had schemed with Creeper to beat the system when the system had been beaten all the time by a boy who didn't want an empty, unearned honor. He would tell him about the first two years of college that had been largely wasted in terms of studentship, about Robert Hare's death, about Whiskers and Pete and the library, and about the day Toady Reed and he had brought Lizzie Whitman to the brink of tears. Through these events a pattern had been running: a pattern of growth. When he looked back upon himself through the ivy years, Jeremy saw himself emerging. He was not dissatisfied.

"I can hold a job," he said, and believed it firmly.

He didn't know what job it would be, and he didn't much care. He would find it as he had found the old German doctor who had told him to seek his refuge in education. He would find it as he had found the greatness in Twissy, the gift of objectivity through Silvers, a love of books through Pete. Perhaps the job didn't exist, and then he would create it—as Pete said Darwin had created his theory of evolution practically all in a day when he had stumbled upon one of Sir Charles Lyell's works on geology and suddenly had seen the correlation between his own observations and those of Lyell's. He had background from which to seek, a mind that could grasp truth, eyes that could see. He hadn't thrown away the ivy years completely.

Jeremy stopped leaning against the bridge railing. He was tired and hungry. He walked back slowly, planning to call Agnes after supper. He supposed Will was home by now. Passing Old Queen's he saw a light burning in Silvers's office. He went in to tell him about Will.

"I know, Jeremy. Will told me he was going to tell you."

"I didn't mind as much as I thought I would four years ago."

Silvers smiled. He saw no reason for telling Jeremy he had waited past his usual train in case he hadn't been able to take it this way.

"You're not worried about me, are you, sir?"

Silvers shook his head. On the way to the train he mailed a letter to the president of the university, explaining why Jeremy was the man he wanted to be his assistant editor of university publications.

III

Muggsy possessed a genius for doing things backward. All through February, March, and the frequently chill rains of April Muggsy had gone without so much as a sniffle, but now that May had arrived, warm and dry and sunny, Muggsy's eyes were puffed out and his temples throbbed wickedly.

"A head cold," diagnosed the university physician, staring in fascination at the collection of medicines on the top of Muggsy's bureau. "Come on over to the infirmary and we'll put you to bed."

An hour later Muggsy lay in a clean white bed on the second floor of Pell Hall, three pillows behind his back, a thermometer in his mouth, and a nurse adjusting the venetian blinds so that the sun wouldn't disturb him. Muggsy was attracted at once to the nurse's trim figure and pleasant face; always a gentleman willing to rise to any occasion, Muggsy contrived to wink amorously over the tip of the slanting thermometer.

"Something in your eye?" the nurse asked solicitously.

Muggsy shook his head, inwardly crushed. Women never seemed to take him seriously. Not that it mattered. This was the day he wrote to Flo, and the least he could do was to keep his mind free of the temptation of other females. Tomorrow he wrote to Midge. The day after to Joan—but Muggsy wasn't quite sure of Joan. Maybe that scented stationery she used had irritated his nasal passages and made him susceptible to this confounded cold.

"No fever," said the nurse. "You'll be out of here in the morning. Bring anything to study?"

"Yes'm."

"Ring if you need anything."

"Yes'm."

"And don't smoke abed."

"No ma'am. I never smoke beds. I tried it once, but it made me dizzy. Must have been inhaling the mattress, I imagine."

Exasperated, the nurse closed the door behind her.

Muggsy rested his back against the pillows, chuckling. If the nurse thought his puns were terrible, she should hear his father's. Muggsy sighed at his awareness of his own shortcomings, all of which he intended to correct the day after tomorrow. In the entire university he doubted if anyone could surpass him for putting off until tomorrow what absolutely didn't have to be done today. And where did it get him? Here he was with a head that felt filled with glue, and tomorrow morning he had to turn in a term paper in his course in international relations. At least two thousand words on "Weaknesses in the Structure of the League of Nations"—what a stinker of a subject! Of course the whole course wasn't any better—not taught by that little pinhead who strutted around in front of the class and sprung a quiz every Saturday morning so that he could sit in a corner and quietly snooze. Thus far Muggsy had written the title of the term paper on the first page of a long yellow pad and had unearthed in the library a copy of *Time Magazine* that contained an analytical article concerning the pros and cons of the League. He was ready for the labor.

Muggsy worked in his own peculiar manner. He read *Time* for a while, composed part of his letter to Flo, gave that up for a chapter in his textbook, poured over his illegibly scrawled lecture notes, gazed off into space thinking about the nurse, went back to his letter to Flo, read some more in *Time,* and at long last began to scrawl on the long yellow pages. In this way he succeeded in finishing the letter to Flo, reading twice through the article in *Time,* and completing the term paper. The paper was good enough, he thought; it would pass. Somehow he had always managed to pass, not with too much distinction except in European history. Muggsy let his head fall back against the pillow and wondered if it were possible to marry a girl without kissing her first.

Next morning Muggsy was released from the infirmary and left his term paper in international relations at the instructor's office. Within a week he had forgotten it almost entirely. Jeremy had gone over to Jameson to see Agnes when Muggsy called him on the telephone.

"I'm out of college," Muggsy said. His voice was old and tired and convincing.

"But Muggsy, what—"

"They've had me up before a committee of the faculty. That term paper in international relations. They say I plagiarized whole paragraphs from the article in *Time.*"

"Did you?"

There was a pause, then a sound suspiciously like a sob. "I don't know, Jeremy. It seems so. They've got me confused."

"You wait right there," Jeremy directed and hung up the receiver.

The sight of Muggsy was a shock. He had a stunned, red-eyed blurriness that made him look like a middle-aged man. Sitting on the edge of the bed, he clasped and unclasped his hands nervously. He tried to smile, but all of the old bravado that always had been his shield against the world was gone now.

"Mother and father are going to take this badly," he said dully. "It's going to embarrass them with all their friends as well as break their hearts."

"Did you mean to cheat, Muggsy?"

"No. I just wanted to get the paper done—the easiest way."

"What can they prove?"

"That there are three long paragraphs in my paper almost word for word with the article in *Time*."

"Suppose those paragraphs had been in quotation marks?"

"They weren't."

"But who can prove you didn't mean to insert those quotation marks?"

Muggsy rolled over on the bed, groaning. Who could prove it? The committee hadn't tried to prove it. There before the members had lain paper and article. The committee hadn't paid too much attention to those, either. Only one question really had been asked. Could he as a gentleman feel that he had lived up to the standards of the university? The charge of plagiarism had been substantiated by cold fact, and a little old man with white hair had said, "Boys come into college, but men are supposed to graduate." And another member of the committee had explained how in college he had been careless once and had done practically what Muggsy had done and had flunked the course. There had been one big difference, of course; he had flunked in his freshman year, whereas Muggsy was a senior, and his flunking meant not graduating with his class but coming back to summer school to make up the course. No one really had recriminated; everyone seemed to understand how it had happened; and there was only the one question to answer; how about standards? Muggsy knew what they meant. They were sorry, but the decision had to go against him. Without standards no university could long exist.

"You could fight them," Jeremy said.

"Legally, with a smart lawyer, I might win," Muggsy agreed. "I've thought of that. There's only one thing wrong with that."

Muggsy crawled across the bed and pulled his suitcase from the closet. Once you busted out there was only one thing to do. Get off the campus.

"What was wrong with it, Muggsy?"

"It's no way to get a degree—in a court room. For the first time today I think I learned that marks and degrees and even Phi Beta Kappa keys don't mean much. You know your own value. The standards are there as your measure, not the university's. And if they had given me a phony degree wouldn't that make your degree phony also, since we were classmates—almost were, anyhow."

Jeremy watched Muggsy begin to throw his socks into his suitcase. "You never wanted to grow up, Muggsy."

"I do now. If they can't teach you one way you have to be taught in another."

Muggsy's voice caught. His underwear went into his suitcase, a badly rumpled mess.

IV

"Say," the tipsy man said, "let me tell you how it happened." The tipsy man had removed his coat and vest and had unloosed his suspenders, for the tipsy man was very warm and the last drink hadn't improved his condition. Jeremy, standing timidly at the entrance to the tent that housed the reunion of the Class of 1908, found it difficult to remember that at luncheon in the gymnasium that afternoon the tipsy man had presented to the university on behalf of his class a check for several thousands of dollars. The president had called the tipsy man a credit to the old school, and a fine upright citizen, but Jeremy thought that the only thing which was keeping the tipsy man upright at the moment was suspension of the laws of gravity.

Iron Man said, "He was some football player, that guy. About the greatest plunging back this school ever produced."

"That big glob of fat?"

"Yes, sir," said Iron Man. "He was fast."

Jeremy shook his head. Everything about class reunion night astonished him. In other years he had gone home for vacation and had missed the festivities that went on when the alumni came back on the evening before commencement. They were all over the campus, some of them dressed like firemen, others like hula hula dancers with bony knees sticking out from under synthetic grass skirts. One class had a water wagon that its members carted around the campus wherever they went, and another class travelled in a hay wagon driven by a darky in nondescript overalls and a high silk hat. Down at the other end of the campus green and red flares illuminated the night; beyond was the tent of the Class of 1911 where Jeremy had encountered the skinny man who had wanted to steal the clapper out of the bell in Old Queen's. But nobody would go along with him, and the skinny man was feeling very sad. He had sat on a stool, holding the stem of a carnation between his teeth, and had refused to talk to anybody.

"Do you think we'll be like this twenty-five or thirty years from now?" Jeremy asked Iron Man.

Iron Man said "sssh!" rather sternly, for the tipsy man was ready to go on with his story.

"Never was a game quite like it," the tipsy man said. "Snow all over the field. You'd get tackled an' it'd get down

inside your drawers an' you'd dance around tryin' to get it
out. Well, we're playin' Hamilton that day an' it's tough.
Tougher even than old Scotty used to be when you flunked
one of his exams. I'm having a hell of a time in that game
'cause I busted my shoulder against N.Y.U. the week before.
Or was it Princeton? Anyway, that shoulder hurt an' the
coach had strapped a piece of raw beef to it to ease the rub of
the pads against my skin. I'm like a hootchie kootchie dancer
with the seven-year itch. Every time those Hamilton boys hit
me that beef slips an' I have to reach in an' pull it back into
place. Finally I says to myself, 'To hell with that,' and I
reaches in an' pulls out this hunk of soggy beef an' fling it on
the ground. Honest, I thought those Hamilton boys would
die right there. They didn't know what it was—my heart or
a hunk off one of my ribs or maybe they had disemboweled
me. They simply never got over the shock. We run a couple
of plays an' there was nothin' to it. They just folded up; that
bloody mess layin' there in the snow was too much for 'em!"

Iron Man laughed until his belly began to ache. Jeremy
thought the story funny, but not that funny. The tipsy man
unbuttoned his shirt.

Jeremy was suddenly dog-tired. Tomorrow he would
graduate; the ivy years would end. Mom and pop were coming down to see him in his cap and gown, and Agnes was
coming for commencement also. He slipped away from the
tent and went slowly along the path that led over Holy Hill
to Hegeman. Tonight was the last time he would walk this
path as an undergraduate. The noise of the alumni reunions
seemed to fill the campus with happy, exciting echoes.

At the foot of Holy Hill the man stopped him. The old
chap's hair was mostly white and his tie was long and flowing,
the neckwear of another generation. In the light from the
overhead street lamp the lettering was discernible on the button on the lapel of the old gentleman's coat. It said: Class of
1891.

"Good evening, son."

"Good evening, sir."

"Graduating tomorrow?"

"Yes, sir."

"Been a long time since I was in your shoes, boy."

"So I see by your button, sir."

"Mighty good class, 1891. One of the best. Ministers and lawyers and all good Republicans. Fine men. Class of 1892 wasn't so good as I remember. Had a Democrat. And as if that wasn't bad enough, had a horse thief too. Could have forgiven that, though."

Jeremy laughed.

"Know what's up there in those shadows on the hill, boy?"

"No, sir, I don't."

"Well, I'll tell you, boy. My youth's up there. If you should happen to see it going up the steps, tell the rascal there's an old man comes back looking for it every year and never loses hope that he'll catch just one small, quick glimpse of it."

"Yes, sir, I'll do that."

"Well, God bless you, boy, and good luck and good night. I'll be looking for you in the academic procession tomorrow."

Jeremy went on. He began to realize that a good part of his own youth already had escaped into those same dark shadows of Holy Hill.

V

On prom nights groups of townspeople had gathered around the entrance to the gymnasium, watching the couples as they arrived and admiring the pretty dresses. To Jeremy there always had been something exhilarating in that experience, an artificial but nonetheless pleasurable glow of importance and elevation, and the way the girls laughed and ran up the gym steps had revealed that they also were pleased. Commencement was simply a prom night multiplied a hundredfold; all the way along College Avenue the sidewalk was thronged with townspeople, alumni and perspiring, gawping, smiling parents waiting for the academic procession from Old Queen's to the gymnasium; there was a feeling of anticipation in the air almost tantamount to the feeling on a football Saturday when the pennant vendors, the program salesmen, and the old men with their bunches of chrysanthemums were hawking their wares everywhere you stepped.

Pop had worn a new suit and mom a new dress and a hat that was mostly all fluff and veil. Jeremy felt choked up when he realized what a big day this was for them, too. He thought of poor old Muggsy, who would read of commencement in the papers tomorrow morning, and of Robert Hare's blind father and mother who would be remembering that this was the day their son should have graduated. Four years ago Jeremy's class had numbered almost five hundred, but less than three hundred were graduating today. In the difference between those two figures many stories were told: of the boy who had committed suicide in the Sourland Mountains, of chaps like Muggsy who had learned in the hard, grim way the meaning of standards, of others who had been forced to drop by the way because of financial difficulties, tempermental instability, or plain foolishness. Commencement was both a happy and a sad day.

Pop stood with his arm around Agnes. Pop liked Agnes; he called her his sweetheart and told Jeremy it was lucky for him his old father wasn't twenty-five years younger or somebody's nose would have been out of joint. "A fine girl," pop had said the first time he had met Agnes. Jeremy had answered, self-conscious, wondering about the sacrifices pop and mom had made for his education, "We hope to be married when I have a steady job." But pop had seemed to think that was fine. "Of course I'll remember what I owe you and mom," Jeremy had said, wanting pop to understand where he stood. For a moment pop's eyes had appeared a trifle clouded, and then he had said, "It doesn't work that way,

boy. We've always found our happiness in you; that's something you don't need to repay. There's really only one thing
more your mother and I expect out of you." Jeremy had
asked, "And that, sir?" Pop had laughed. "Grandchildren,
you boob. Maybe I better talk that over with Agnes." Jeremy
had blushed and pop's laughter had grown heartier.

Standing between Duncan Faust and Iron Man as the marshal of the procession went along the lines with a worried
look, Jeremy glanced down at pop and Agnes and felt humbled. Maybe pop didn't have as much formal education as he,
but pop possessed the thing that counted. Character. Pop was
a mighty fine man. Jeremy still had the bookrack pop had
made with the nail holes filled with putty; he intended to
keep it always. As a remembrance of the ivy years and of pop
and of the sweet, tender beauty of unselfishness.

"It's hot," Duncan growled. "This cap and gown was designed for an eskimo."

"Two bucks to rent these things for one day," Iron Man
complained. "Everything about this place is a racket."

Jeremy thought two dollars was a cheap price to pay for
the satisfaction of wearing a cap and gown. He was a little
concerned about the tassel on his mortar board and kept feeling it with his hand to make sure it hung on the right side.
After he received his degree, the tassel went on the left side;
in chapel two days ago when the details of commencement
had been explained, quite a point had been made of this academic tradition symbolizing the turn from undergraduate to
graduate.

"They're moving up ahead," Iron Man said.

Jeremy craned his neck. It was so. The procession had begun. The ivy years that really had started with Iron Man's
friendship were ending with Iron Man as procession mate.
Jeremy again knew a feeling of chokiness. The memory of all
he was leaving behind came over him suddenly—those long
nights on *Targum,* climbing the stairs in Van Nest for a class

with Twissy, Sunday worship in the chapel, Hegeman and bull sessions and the mounting excitement of an approaching football game, the cold, lonely walks back from Jameson, the talks with Silvers, watching Pete on a lecture platform lighting one cigarette from another, Muggsy morose over his turned-out navel or the infidelity of the female of the species, the bizarre costumes of initiates during Hell Week, going up to the gymnasium for the Robeson concert or a basketball game or a swimming meet, the visiting lecturer whom nobody understood completely, not even the smarties like Whiskers and Julius Lang, a winter afternoon in the library, proms and hops and meetings of the Barbarians, Robert Hare reading from Wordsworth and Lizzie Whitman reading from Browning, the attic room in Spook's Hole and Kathie in her hair curlers, the rides to Easton and Bethlehem and Worcester for football games, the sandwich route and rehearsals for "Skit Night," scheming to hoodwink the dean of men, exam times and lecture notes and piles of unread books, the summer vacations that had dragged at the end, Mildred Hawes, the battle of Darwinism and Iron Man going off to class with an alarm clock under his arm . . . the memories were like a flood that seemed to have no ending once they broke through the gates of consciousness. Miss Sprig. Mr. Kelly with his persuasive patter about books. Visch going off to Perth Amboy to work on his model dental drills. Old Dr. Will. Charlie the Bat in Abraham's Bosom. Jeremy wished fervently that the ivy years were just starting. They had been wonderful.

The procession had moved across the campus to College Avenue. He lost sight of mom and pop and Agnes, but all along the way there were other faces he quickly recognized: Mrs. Louie, Mrs. Bridewell leaning on her cane, Creeper back for reunion, the tipsy man who had won a football game with a slab of raw beef, the campus cops, the crowd who worked in the library, and Iron Man's father and mother who clapped proudly when their son marched by.

Almost to the gymnasium, Jeremy began to wonder about the old gentleman from the Class of 1891 who had stopped him last night at the foot of Holy Hill. He had been watching for him all the while and was disappointed that he hadn't seen him. It was too late now; they had reached the gymnasium; here the procession divided and the faculty and honorary degree recipients stood on both sides of the street so that the seniors could walk through and be the first to enter the gymnasium. Jeremy felt solemn and self-conscious as he moved ahead; then, almost to the doors, he saw the old gentleman from the Class of 1891.

"Him?" Iron Man said. "I don't know his name but he's some big shot. They're giving him an honorary degree."

Jeremy shook his head. How typical of all the ivy years—this rubbing elbows with men who were celebrities. Just part of the crowd. Your crowd. When Jeremy looked up the old gentleman's glance crossed his own. The man winked.

A smile came softly to Jeremy's lips. The president probably thought the old gentleman had come back for his degree, but Jeremy knew better. Up there among the dark shadows of Holy Hill last night had lurked that elusive rascal who had been the real attraction. Year after year he was there. Perhaps he was never found, but he was never lost, either. Part of an old college song came back to Jeremy then:

> *My heart clings closer than the ivy,*
> *As life runs out its fleeting span,*
> *To those hallowed, classic halls,*
> *And those ivy-covered walls,*
> *On the banks of the old Raritan.*